# Electronic Circuit Action Series

## Series

# RADIO CIRCUITS

by Thomas M. Adams
Captain, U.S. Navy, Retired

HOWARD W. SAMS & CO., INC.

THE BOBBS-MERRILL CO., INC.

INDIANAPOLIS · KANSAS CITY · NEW YORK

SECOND EDITION

THIRD PRINTING — 1968

Library of Congress Catalog Card Number: 66-24121

# PREFACE

This book is presented as a logical follow up to the four previously published volumes in this series. The circuits analyzed are the basic types widely used in various amplitude-modulated receiver systems. The analytical technique is the same as in the previous texts—namely, to make a positive identification of each and every electron current flowing in the circuit under consideration, and then to thoroughly describe the movements of that current so that its underlying function or purpose will be made clear. In this, as in the other volumes, electron currents have been treated as if they were actually moving parts in a piece of mechanical machinery; when this approach is used, it is much easier to understand the relationship of each current to every other current.

Individual circuits are discussed in the first five chapters. The last three chapters present analyses of a table model superheterodyne radio, a transistorized superheterodyne radio, and a TRF receiver. Standard maintenance tests—voltage checking and signal substitution—have been discussed in detail. These tests are normally performed by the technician or maintenance man; however, an understanding of the significance of the various steps in these procedures can teach both student technicians and engineering students about what happens inside circuits. Voltage checking and signal substitution enable the technician to make a judgment on almost every component in the radio by observing something about one or more of the predicted electron currents at each of the many test points. Normally the presence or absence of a particular current, or a substantial change in its value, will enable the student to determine what component is at fault.

Occasionally, a circuit component carries several electron currents simultaneously; however, the majority of components will be found to carry one or, at the most, two separate electron currents during normal operation. The circuit diagrams in Chapters 6 and 7 enable you to "envision" each of these currents. The test procedures then give you a means of knowing whether the expected current is actually present. Any deviation from the expected amount of a particular current can lead to a usually obvious deduction as to which component is not performing properly.

Every attempt has been made to keep the discussions as simple as possible; little or no background in electronics or mathematics is necessary to understand the text material. Because the basic electron current approach used is necessary to students of all levels in electronics, this book is considered neither too advanced for high school and technical institute training, nor too elementary for college level.

THOMAS M. ADAMS

# TABLE OF CONTENTS

## CHAPTER 1

## CHAPTER 2

## CHAPTER 3

## CHAPTER 4

## CHAPTER 5

## CHAPTER 6

# CHAPTER 7

# CHAPTER 8

Chapter 1

# HETERODYNING ACTIONS

The mixer circuit combines two different radio-frequency currents in order to obtain a third current, usually of lower frequency, whose modulations will be a true representation of the modulations carried by one of the two original currents. In receivers one of these two original currents is called the *carrier*, or *signal*, current. This current is the one which is being received from a transmitting station. The other of the two original currents is generated within the receiver by a separate oscillator circuit and is usually referred to as the *local oscillator* current, or oscillator current.

In general, it is less difficult to construct circuits that will amplify low-frequency currents than it is to construct them for high-frequency currents. Thus, in receiver work it is almost universal practice to "step down" the carrier frequency by some process such as mixing two currents and getting a third current, before amplifying the signal.

## TRIODE MIXER

The triode mixer circuit, while not too common in present-day receivers, is the basic mixer circuit. Figs. 1-1, 1-2, and 1-3 demonstrate the operation of this circuit.

### Identification of Components

The components which make up this circuit are identified as follows:

C1—Grid tuned-tank capacitor.
C2—RF filter capacitor.
C3—Plate tuned-tank capacitor.
T1—First RF transformer.
T2—Second RF transformer.
T3—IF transformer.
V1—Triode vacuum tube used as mixer.
M1—Antenna.
M2—Grid biasing-voltage source.

## Identification of Currents

Four different electron currents, each flowing at a different frequency are present in Figs. 1-1, 1-2, and 1-3. These electron currents are each shown in color and are identified as follows:

1. Current at carrier or signal frequency (red).
2. Current at oscillator frequency (blue).
3. Current at difference frequency (solid green).
4. Current at sum frequency (dotted green).

## Circuit Operation

The first current to be discussed is the radio-frequency carrier current being received at the antenna. This current carries the modulation, or intelligence, which is intended to be amplified and demodulated. Although the primary of T1 has been shown as connected directly to the antenna, the signal current may be passed through an RF amplifier stage before being subjected to the mixing or frequency-changing process. (The mixer stage was formerly referred to as the "first detector," to differentiate it from the demodulator stage; however, this terminology is seldom used in modern practice.)

Fig. 1-1 shows the currents which will flow in this circuit *when the local oscillator is not energized.* (The local oscillator is connected to the primary winding of T2.) Only a single half-cycle of operation is shown in Fig. 1-1; it is the half-cycle when the signal current makes the control grid negative, thereby cutting off any current flow through the tube. However, the previous half-cycle would have permitted a pulsation of current to flow through the tube, and consequently, the remnants of this tube current are seen flowing off filter capacitor C2 and exiting downward through the primary winding of T3 to the power supply. At the same time a component of filter current at this frequency is shown re-entering the lower plate of C2.

The tuned tank, composed of C3 and the primary of T3 in the plate circuit, is not resonant at this carrier frequency; therefore no oscillation will be set up in the tank due to a pulsation of current which repeats itself at this frequency.

Fig. 1-2 shows a half-cycle of circuit operation *when there is a local oscillator current but no signal current.* The local oscillator current is shown (in blue) flowing through the lower, or primary, winding of T2, thereby supporting a current at the same frequency in the grid tank circuit.

The half-cycle chosen for Fig. 1-2 is one which makes the grid positive so that plate current is flowing through the tube. This current is shown *entering* the top plate of filter capacitor C2 before flowing to the power supply through the primary of T3.

Fig 1-3 shows the conditions when the carrier and oscillator currents both exist simultaneously in the grid circuit. As an example of the frequencies involved, if the carrier signal being received were from a broadcast station operating at 1,000 kc per second, the local oscillator would be operating at a higher frequency, such as 1,500 kc per second. Thus, a million complete cycles of the current shown in red will flow back and forth in the grid tank each second. Also, it is known that one-million-five-hundred-thousand cycles of the current shown in blue will flow in the grid-tank circuit each second. Each one will attempt to act independently in turning the electron stream on and off in the tube. When the two currents are momentarily in phase they will be aiding each other. Conversely, when they are momentarily out of phase with each other, or in "opposite phase," they will oppose and neutralize each other.

Pulsations of current are released through the tube at both frequencies, although the sizes of the pulsations will vary from cycle to cycle, depending on the extent to which each of the grid driving current-voltage combinations is augmented or cancelled by partial combinations with the other. The size of filter capacitor C2 is chosen so that it will have low reactance at both frequencies. Thus pulsations are effectively filtered back to ground through this capacitor, while the electrons themselves may continue their journey to the power supply after passing through the primary winding of T3.

The formula for determining the reactance of a capacitor at any frequency is:

$$X_c = \frac{1}{2\pi fC}$$

where,

$X_c$ is the capacitive reactance in ohms,
f is the frequency of the current in question in cycles per second,
C is the capacitance in farads.

9

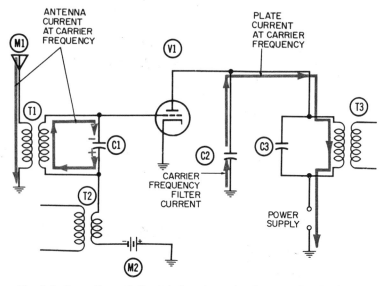

Fig. 1-1. Operation of the triode mixer circuit—negative half-cycle, no oscillator current.

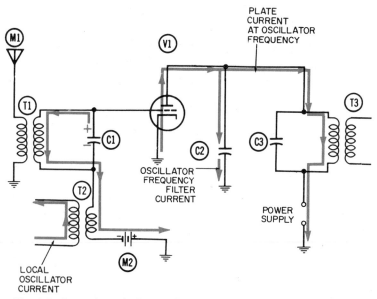

Fig. 1-2. Operation of the triode mixer circuit—positive half-cycle, no carrier current.

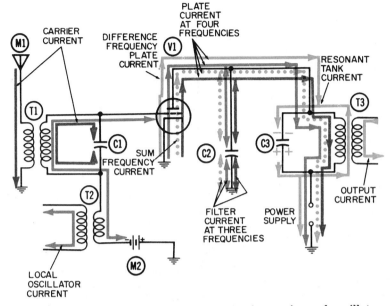

Fig. 1-3. Operation of the triode mixer circuit—carrier and oscillator currents both present.

The capacitive reactance is a measure of the opposition which a capacitor will offer to electron flow. From this formula it can be seen that the opposition varies inversely to both the frequency and the size of the capacitor. Thus, any capacitor offers less opposition to the flow of high-frequency currents than to those of lower frequency, and also a larger capacitor offers less opposition to the flow of any current at any frequency than does a smaller capacitor.

In addition to pulsations of current going through the tube at the carrier and the oscillator frequencies, pulsations also occur at two other principal frequencies, called the sum and difference frequencies. It can be demonstrated mathematically that when two sine waves of differing frequencies are combined, or added, these two additional frequencies, along with numerous others of lesser importance in this case, will be created. The sum of the two original frequencies is 2,500 kc. In Fig. 1-3 a new current is shown completing the filtering process through C2, and flowing out to the power supply essentially as DC. This current is shown in dotted green, and is labeled as the *sum* frequency. Since its frequency is considerably higher than either of the original frequencies, we know from the foregoing reactance formula that the pulsations at this frequency will be filtered by C2 with even greater ease than are the original frequencies.

A fourth current has been shown in solid green in Fig. 1-3. This current is intended to represent the *difference* frequency. Using the 1,000-kc carrier frequency and the 1,500-kc oscillator frequency, as before, the difference frequency is 500 kc. Capacitor C3 and the primary of T3 are tuned to be resonant at this frequency; hence, the recurring pulsations will build up a sizable tank current at this frequency. Transformer action across T3 will build up a current-voltage combination at this same difference frequency in the grid circuit of the next amplifier stage.

All four currents are shown crossing the tube in Fig. 1-3. This signifies that the plate current carries pulsations at all four of the frequencies under consideration. The pulsations at the three highest frequencies are shown entering the upper plate of filter capacitor C2; filtering currents at these frequencies are shown moving between the lower plate and ground. However, the fourth current (in solid green), representing the important difference frequency, is shown flowing directly to the tuned plate circuit, where it arrives in the proper phase to reinforce the oscillation which exists there at that frequency. The plate tank is constructed and tuned to be resonant only at this difference frequency.

It is a characteristic of mixing or conversion circuits of this type that the modulation of the carrier signal, which represents the desired intelligence being received is conveyed or transplanted intact to the new lower-frequency current, called the difference-frequency. Thus, in later stages of amplification, even though a lower frequency is being amplified, the intelligence of modulation it carries is a faithful reproduction of the original modulation which will eventually be demodulated from the difference frequency. The output current shown in Fig. 1-3 is caused to flow by the transformer action of T3. It flows at the same frequency as the difference frequency and has the same modulation characteristic, or "envelope," as existed on the original signal current received from the station.

The output current-voltage combination from a mixer circuit is usually referred to as the intermediate frequency, or IF, because it is between the signal current and the audio range in the frequency spectrum.

Unlike most of the circuit diagrams in this text, Fig. 1-3 depicts *many* cycles of the three higher frequencies, while showing a single half-cycle of the lowest, or difference frequency, in the plate circuit resonant tank. It is for this reason that arrows are shown in both directions in the grid and filter circuits.

## PENTAGRID MIXER CIRCUIT

Another effective means of mixing voltages of two different radio frequencies is shown in Figs. 1-4, 1-5, and 1-6. This arrangement involves the use of two vacuum tubes.

### Identification of Components

The pentagrid mixer circuit contains the following components:

R1—Grid-drive and grid-return resistor.
R2—Cathode-biasing resistor.
R3—Screen-grid dropping resistor.
R5—Power-supply decoupling resistor.
C1—RF tank capacitor, working in conjunction with L2.
C2—Coupling capacitor between local oscillator and mixer.
C3—Screen-grid filter capacitor.
C4—Plate-tank capacitor.
C7—Power-supply decoupling capacitor.
L1—Primary winding of input RF transformer.
L2—Secondary winding of same transformer.
L3—Plate-tank inductor.
V1—Pentagrid mixer tube.

The local oscillator circuit contains the following components:

R4—Grid-leak biasing resistor.
C5—Oscillator tank capacitor.
C6—Grid-leak capacitor.
L4—Oscillator tickler coil.
L5—Oscillator tank coil.
V2—Triode oscillator tube.

### Identification of Currents

There are a total of 11 significant currents during normal operation of the circuit in Figs. 1-4, 1-5, and 1-6. These currents, and the colors they are shown in are:

1. Input or "signal" radio-frequency current (solid blue).
2. V1 plate current (solid red).
3. Plate-tank current (dotted blue).
4. V1 screen-grid current (also in solid red).
5. V1 screen-grid filter current (also in solid red).
6. Oscillator-circuit grid-tank current (solid green).
7. Grid-driving current for both tubes (also in solid green).
8. Grid-leakage current from oscillator tube (also in dotted red).
9. V2 plate current (also in solid red).

10. Feedback current (dotted green).
11. High-frequency decoupling currents (in both solid blue and solid green).

## Details of Operation

As is the case with all frequency-mixing, or *heterodyning*, circuits, one of the two voltages to be mixed is the signal voltage; and the other one is a voltage generated locally in the oscillator portion of the circuit. The purpose of the mixing process is to obtain a new and lower frequency, because lower frequencies are easier to handle and amplify.

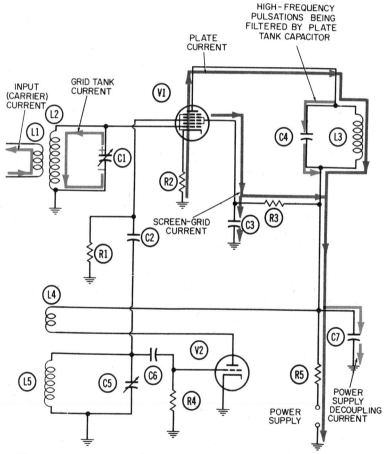

Fig. 1-4. Operation of the pentagrid mixer circuit—local oscillator not operating.

*Local Oscillator Not Operating*—Fig. 1-4 shows the relatively few currents which flow when the local oscillator is not operating and a signal current is being received. The signal current is received from the antenna and flows in inductor L1. In Fig. 1-4 it is shown flowing upward through L1 and inducing a companion current to flow downward in L2. Since the tank circuit composed of L2 and C1 is tuned to the particular frequency being received, the current induced in L2 will quickly set up an oscillation of electrons in the tuned circuit.

Fig. 1-4 depicts the half-cycle of oscillation when the upper plate of C1 is made positive. Since the first control grid of V1 is connected directly to the top of this tank, the voltage on this

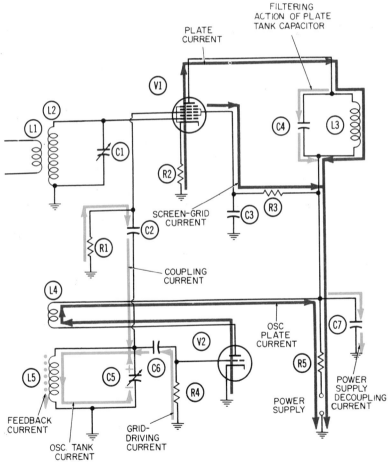

**Fig. 1-5. Operation of the pentagrid mixer circuit—no input carrier signal.**

grid will be identical with the voltage at the top of the tank at all times. During positive half-cycles, such as in Fig. 1-4, plate current through mixer tube V1 will be increased. During the next succeeding half-cycle, when the top of the tuned tank exhibits a negative voltage, this same plate current will be reduced.

Thus the voltage variations of the tuned tank, which are occurring at the frequency of the carrier signal being received, will impose pulsations on the plate current stream at this same frequency. The plate current flows through plate-tank inductor L3 and on through the power supply and back to ground. Inductor L3 and capacitor C4 form a resonant tank circuit at the difference frequency, or IF. Consequently, the pulsations in plate current which occur at the signal frequency are unable to excite the tank circuit into oscillation.

Since the screen grid which surrounds the second control grid within the tube is connected through a resistor to the positive power supply, it will attract and "capture" a large number of electrons from the plate-current stream going through the tube. These captured electrons become the screen-grid current (also shown in solid red in Fig. 1-4) which flows through R3 and rejoins the plate current as it enters the power supply.

*No Signal Conditions*—Fig. 1-5 shows the currents which flow when the local oscillator is operating, but no carrier signal is being received. The oscillator is a standard type, known as a tickler-coil oscillator, in which energy is fed back from the plate to the grid circuit in the appropriate phase to support the oscillation.

The oscillator works in the following manner. When positive voltage is first applied to the plate of V2, it draws an initial surge of plate-current electrons across the tube. This current must flow through L4 on its way to the power supply. As it surges, or accelerates, upward through L4, it induces, by the electromagnetic induction process which occurs between inductors, a companion current to surge *downward* through L5. This is the tickler action, and the induced, or companion, current becomes the feedback current which is shown in dotted green. This feedback current moves in the downward direction and tends to remove electrons from the upper plate of tank capacitor C5 and deliver them to the lower plate. The preceeding makes the upper plate positive; the control grid of V2 is made positive at the same time by the action of the grid driving current which is attracted upward through grid resistor R4 by the positive tank voltage.

The initial surge of feedback current in L5 sets up the condition of resonance in the tank circuit, which is tuned to a new frequency that is known as the *local oscillator frequency*. Thus, on the next succeeding half-cycle, the top of the tank will be at a negative voltage, and the control grid will stop the flow of plate current through V2. The tube thus conducts intermittently rather than continuously, and the plate current is a special case of pulsating DC.

The feedback current generates and supports the oscillating tank current (shown in solid green). In addition to driving the control grid of V2, this tank current and its companion tank voltage also drive the second control grid of mixer tube V1. When the voltage on the top of C5 is positive (Fig. 1-5), it attracts electrons toward it from both directions, namely, upward through resistors R1 and R4. Thus, the control grids to which these resistors are attached will be made positive. On a negative half-cycle, when the voltage at the top of C5 is negative, both grid driving currents will be driven away from the tank, and consequently, will flow downward through the two resistors, making both control grids negative.

The action of the grid driving current in flowing up and down through R1 affords a means of imposing pulsations on the plate-current stream through tube V1; these pulsations will occur at the local oscillator frequency. Since the plate tank is tuned to a much lower frequency, these pulsations of plate current do not excite the plate tank into oscillation. All of the plate current flows through the inductor and on to the power supply, being joined at the entrance to the power supply by the screen-grid current previously described.

The pulsations in the plate current are filtered by plate-tank capacitor C4. This applies to both of the special cases just described. The local oscillator and the carrier signal frequencies are considerably higher than the resonant frequency of the plate-tank circuit. Resonance is defined as a condition wherein the capacitive reactance is equal to the inductive reactance. As the frequency is increased, the reactance of the capacitor decreases and the reactance of the inductor increases. This is stated by the two reactance formulas, which tell us that capacitive reactance is inversely proportional to frequency and that inductive reactance is directly proportional to frequency.

Figs. 1-4 and 1-5 show an individual pulsation of plate current flowing momentarily onto the upper plate of tank capacitor C4 and driving an equal number of electrons out of the lower plate toward the power supply. During the time period between two successive positive half-cycles, the actual electrons which made up the pulsation in the first place will be drawn off the upper plate of C4 and into the power supply by flowing through inductor L3. Also, during this period, the filter action completes itself, and electrons flow back into the lower plate of C4.

The filter current in Fig. 1-4 is shown in blue, since it flows at the same frequency as the carrier signal being received. In Fig. 1-5 it is shown in green, since it flows at the frequency of the local oscillator.

Some arrangement must be provided for bypassing these pulsations around the power supply. The most common arrangement for performing this function is the simple resistor-capacitor combination known as a decoupling network. R5 and C7 form the decoupling network in this example. When the unfiltered pulsations reach the junction of these two components, the path through the resistor appears as a relatively high impedance, whereas C7

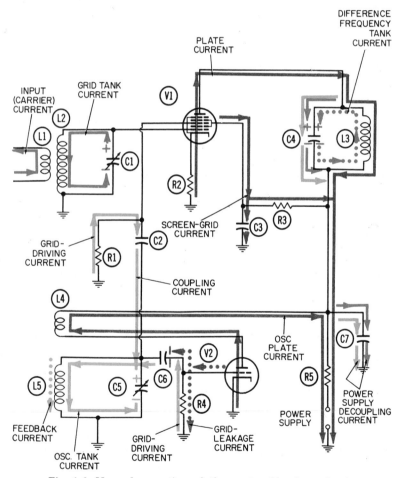

Fig. 1-6. Normal operation of the pentagrid mixer circuit.

has been chosen to have almost negligible reactance or impedance at all radio frequencies. Consequently, when each pulsation is filtered through the plate tank by C4, it is again filtered past the power supply by C7 (Fig. 1-4 and 1-5).

The triode oscillator tube operates under Class-C conditions, which means that the tube conducts less than 50% of each cycle. This is accomplished by using grid-leak biasing. The grid-leakage current has been shown in dotted red in Fig. 1-6. During each positive half-cycle in the oscillator tank, the grid of V2 will be made positive, attracting some electrons from the plate-current stream going through the tube. These electrons, once they strike the control grid, cannot be re-emitted within the tube; they must exit from the tube and flow back to ground through grid resistor R4. Because of the high value of R4, the electrons cannot flow immediately to ground; instead, they will accumulate on the right hand plate of C6, building up a permanent biasing voltage until they can leak downward through R4.

The instantaneous grid voltage varies around this value of negative biasing voltage. Some electrons flow into C6 during each positive half-cycle, and the discharging process through R4 goes on continuously. During negative half-cycles of the oscillator voltage, the negative grid-driving voltage added to the negative grid-biasing voltage will be sufficient to cut off the plate current and hold it cut off for more than a half of each cycle.

*Full Operation*—Fig. 1-6 shows the sum total of all currents which flow in the mixer circuit during normal operation. Basically, all the currents which flow in the two separate examples discussed previously will also flow during normal operation. The plate current through V1 will be affected by the varying voltages on its two control grids, and the plate current will pulsate simultaneously at each of these two input frequencies. Thus, the two filter actions in C4 and C7 will occur side by side with and independently of each other, as shown in Fig. 1-6.

When two separate voltages of different frequencies are mixed in a circuit such as this one, the plate current pulsates at a number of frequencies in addition to the two applied frequencies. It can be shown mathematically that these pulsations will also occur at the *sum* of the two applied frequencies and at many multiples of this sum, such as twice, three times, etc. It can also be shown that pulsations will occur at the *difference* between the two applied frequencies.

All but one of these additional frequencies will be considerably higher than the resonant frequency of the plate-tank circuit. The diffrence frequency is the lowest one at which pulsations occur in the plate-current stream. Hence, if the plate tank is tuned to resonate at the difference frequency, all the other frequencies will be filtered to ground through C4 and C7, in the same manner that the two primary frequencies are filtered.

An oscillation of electrons (shown in dotted blue in Fig. 1-6) will be set up in the plate-tank circuit at the difference frequency. Each cycle of the oscillation will be reinforced by a single pulsation of plate current. The amplifier stages which follow the mixer tube are tuned to this same frequency so that it is the only one which will be amplified.

In AM broadcast reception a difference frequency or intermediate frequency of 455 kc per second is fairly standard. In higher-frequency reception, such as FM, television, and radar, intermediate frequencies ranging from 1 or 2 mc up to 50 or more are not uncommon.

This feature is important when you consider that most receivers are designed to receive any one of several transmitters which are radiating over a band of frequencies, rather than on a single frequency. Thus, the input tank circuit, consisting of L2 and C1, has to be tunable; at least one of the components must be variable. The normal practice is to use a variable capacitor, as indicated in Fig. 1-4, 1-5, and 1-6.

In the oscillator tuned circuit, we find another variable capacitor, C5. C5 and C1 are usually ganged and varied simultaneously by a single tuning control. All circuit elements are designed so that no matter what frequency of carrier is being received, the oscillator tank-circuit frequency will always differ from it by the same amount, such as 455 kc. When this condition is met, the plate-tank circuit and all subsequent amplifier-tank circuits can be manufactured to resonate at this single frequency without the necessity of any tuning adjustments on the operator's part. This feature allows the following circuits to be designed for maximum gain, sensitivity, etc.

## PENTAGRID CONVERTER CIRCUIT

Figs. 1-7 and 1-8 show two alternate moments in the operation of the pentagrid converter circuit of a radio. This circuit performs several complex and important functions, as follows:

1. It receives the incoming radio-frequency signal from the antenna.
2. It generates an entirely separate oscillation frequency.
3. It mixes or combines these two frequencies into a third frequency, known as the intermediate frequency (IF). This combining process is referred to as *frequency conversion*.

4. It amplifies or increases the strength of this new frequency, to a level much higher than either of the original frequencies.

## Identification of Components

The various components which make up this circuit, along with their functional titles, are as follows:

R1—Grid-leak biasing and driving resistor.
C1—Automatic volume-control (AVC) storage capacitor.
C2—Variable capacitor, controlled by the tuning dial.
C3—Trimmer capacitor.
C4—Variable capacitor in oscillator circuit, controlled by the tuning dial.
C5—Fixed oscillator tank capacitor.
C6—Coupling and isolating capacitor.
L1—Radio-frequency transformer, also called the antenna transformer.
L2—Oscillator inductor, which also serves as an auto-transformer.
T1—IF transformer.
V1—Five-grid vacuum tube used as a frequency converter.

## Identification of Electron Currents

In order to understand everything that is happening inside this circuit you must be able to visualize each electron current at work in it. These currents are as follows:

1. Antenna current (solid blue).
2. RF tank current (also in solid blue).
3. Driving current for second control grid (dotted blue).
4. Oscillator tank current (solid green).
5. Oscillator feedback current (dotted green).
6. Driving current for first control grid (dotted green).
7. Tube plate current (solid red).
8. Grid-leakage current (dotted red).
9. Screen-grid current (also in dotted red).
10. IF plate-tank current (also in dotted blue).
11. Grid-tank current for next stage (also in dotted blue).
12. AVC current (also in solid green).

## Details of Operation

*Transformer Action*—The signal or antenna current in solid blue in Fig. 1-7 is caused to flow up and down through the primary winding of antenna transformer L1 by the so-called radio waves transmitted by a radio station. The frequency with which it changes direction is, of course, equal to the frequency of the signal being received. For example, if your radio is tuned to a station that is broadcasting on a frequency of 1,000 kc, the antenna current makes a million complete journeys up and down through the primary winding of L1 *every second.*

Because of the transformer action between the primary and secondary windings of L1, the RF tank current (also shown in solid blue) is driven by this antenna current. Inductance is a sort of electrical inertia and can be compared with the inertia of mechanical devices. For example, it requires extra effort to get any large stationary object, such as an automobile, moving. However, once it is moving, extra effort is required to bring it to a stop.

Both of the foregoing effects result from mechanical inertia. In electrical inertia, which is called inductance, it is not the mass of the electron that concerns us, but the electrical charge carried by each electron. The principal characteristic of any inductance is that it tries to keep the amount of current flowing through it at a constant value. This property leads us to the transformer action which occurs between the primary and secondary windings of L1. As the amount of antenna current shown in Fig. 1-7 increases or builds up in the upward direction, the amount of RF tank current increases in the downward direction in the secondary winding.

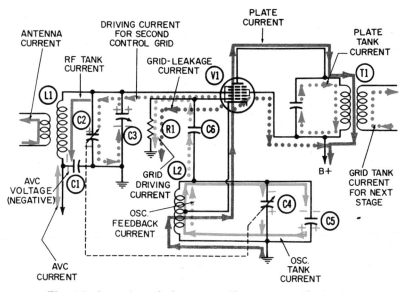

Fig. 1-7. Operation of the pentagrid converter circuit—first control grid negative, second control grid positive.

Similarly, in Fig. 1-8, when the antenna current increases in the downward direction in the primary winding, the RF tank current in the secondary winding increases in the upward direction. An inductance or a transformer responds to *changes* in the amount of driving current, rather than to the intrinsic amount itself. Since the antenna current is constantly changing direction and amount, making a million complete round trips up and down through the primary winding each second, it drives the tank current down and up through the secondary winding at the same frequency.

The RF tank circuit consists of capacitors C2 and C3 in parallel with the secondary winding of transformer L1. In Fig. 1-7 we see a condition where a positive voltage, indicated by plus signs, exists on the upper plates of these two capacitors. This positive voltage exists there because during the previous half cycle, the oscillating electrons have all migrated downward through the second winding, as indicated by the arrows.

In Fig. 1-8 a negative voltage exists on the upper plates of these capacitors. This negative voltage is indicated by minus signs; it results from the fact that during the preceding half-cycle, the tank current electrons migrated upward through the secondary winding, thus delivering a surplus of electrons at the top of the tank. The tank current oscillates continuously between these

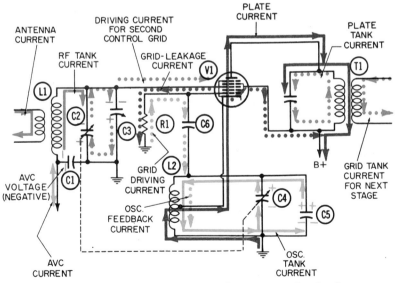

Fig. 1-8. Operation of the pentagrid connector circuit—first control grid positive, second control grid negative.

capacitors and the secondary winding. It is driven or supported in its movements by the antenna current in the primary winding. This tank current oscillation results in the top of the tank exhibiting a voltage that fluctuates from positive to negative at the same frequency as the antenna or signal current. Since the top of the tank is connected directly to the second control grid of the tube V1, this alternating voltage also exists at that control grid and can be used to control, or regulate, the flow of plate-current electrons through V1. The control grid acts like a throttle valve on the electron stream. When the control grid is positive, as in Fig. 1-7, more electrons are allowed to pass through the tube.

When the control grid is negative, as depicted in Fig. 1-8, the quantity of plate-current electrons flowing through the tube will be reduced accordingly.

*Plate Current*—The complete path of plate current, which has been shown in red in both Figs. 1-7 and 1-8, starts at the ground connection below the three components, L2, C4, and C5. The plate current flows through the lower half of inductor L2, then out through the center tap and to the cathode of the tube. The electrons which make up the plate current are then *emitted* into the vacuum of the tube from the heated cathode.

The plate current passes between the wires of all five grids of the tube and strikes the plate of the tube, which absorbs them. They are drawn downward through the primary winding of IF transformer T1, and on to the power supply. The high positive voltage of the power supply is the attractive force which draws the electrons of the plate current (shown in solid red) along the entire path.

*Grid-Leakage Current*—Some electrons which are emitted by the cathode do not reach the plate of the tube, but strike various grid wires and leave the tube as grid current. The grid leakage current (shown in dotted red) which flows downward through resistor R1 is one such grid current. The complete path of this grid-leakage current takes it downward through R1 to ground and then upward through the lower half of L2 to the cathode of the tube, where it is again emitted into the tube.

In continuously flowing downward through R1, this electron current developes a voltage across R1 which is known as a *grid-leak bias voltage*. This voltage is more negative at the top of R1 than at the bottom. This is confirmed by the fact that electrons *always* tend to flow away from an area of more negative voltage toward an area of less negative voltage. This grid-leak voltage provides a stable and fixed negative voltage at the first control grid.

*Oscillating Tank Voltage*—The grid leak bias voltage is not the only one on the first grid. There is an oscillation of electrons occurring in the tank circuit which consists of inductor L2 in parallel with capacitors C4 and C5. The oscillating current has been shown in solid green. Since the top of this tank circuit is connected to the first control grid by means of C6, the oscillating tank voltage is said to be coupled to this grid. In Fig. 1-7 when the voltage at the top of this tank circuit is negative, electrons are driven upward into the lower plate of C6; this action, in turn, drives other electrons away from the upper plate of C6 and downward through R1. The downward flow of electron current through R1 tells us that the top of the resistor is more negative than the bottom during the particular instant represented by the diagram.

An opposite set of conditions is depicted in Fig. 1-8. The tank current (shown in solid green) has reversed itself and flows downward through L2 to the bottom plates of C4 and C5, making them negative with respect to the upper plates. An electron deficiency has been created on the upper plates so that they now exhibit a positive voltage (indicated by plus signs). This positive voltage draws electrons downward from the lower plate of C6, and in turn, draws other electrons upward through biasing and driving resistor R1 and downward to the upper plate of C6. The upward flow of electron current through R1 tells us that the top of this resistor is more positive than the bottom during this particular half-cycle of oscillation.

The current (shown in dotted green) which flows up and down through R1 is labeled as the grid driving current because it "drives" the first control grid by developing an alternating voltage at that grid. This current flows simultaneously with the grid-leakage current, but is completely independent of it. Each current develops its own voltage at the grid; the total voltage at this grid at any instant of time is the algebraic sum of these two separate voltages. The resulting voltage at the first control grid will fluctuate at the same frequency as the oscillator tank current. The result will be that the electron stream flowing through V1 will be increased and decreased at this same frequency. During the half-cycle represented by Fig. 1-7 when the control grid is made most negative, the electron stream, which is in reality the plate current through the tube, will be "throttled back" to a minimum amount.

During the half-cycles represented by Fig. 1-8 when the first control grid is made least negative, this plate current stream will be "turned up" to a maximum value. Hence, the plate current through V1 fluctuates at the oscillator frequency.

*Sustaining Oscillations*—The tank circuit, consisting of L2, C4, and C5, along with the cathode and first control grid of the tube, make up the most essential parts of a conventional Hartley oscillator. No oscillation of electrons can continue to exist unless there is some form of feedback between the output and the input circuits to replenish the inevitable losses. In Figs. 1-7 and 1-8 feedback is obtained by means of the autotransformer action which occurs between the lower portion of inductor L2 and the entire inductor.

Oscillator feedback current has been shown in dotted green in Figs. 1-7 and 1-8. In Fig. 1-8, it is shown in phase with the oscillator tank current (solid green) flowing downward through entire inductor L2. Because the two currents are in phase, the feedback current reinforces or strengthens the oscillator tank current.

*Autotransformer Action*—It is important to understand what causes feedback current to flow in the first place. In Fig. 1-8 when the top of the tank is positive, the control grid reaches its least negative (or most positive) voltage. This permits a surge of plate-current electrons to flow from the cathode into the tube. These electrons must first be drawn upward from ground and through the lower portion of L2. Any inductor will always oppose any increase or decrease in the amount of current which is flowing through it. Consequently, when the plate current flowing upward through the lower portion of L2 is increased, a separate electron current will be generated in the entire inductor, increasing in the downward direction. It is by autotransformer action such as this that an inductor tries to keep the total current through it from changing. This new current is the feedback current. In Fig. 1-7 when the top of the oscillator tank is negative, the voltage at the first control grid has its most negative value. This restricts the flow of plate current through the tube, and of course, it reduces the upward flow of current through the lower portion of L2 by the same amount. The inductor responds in the conventional and expected manner and this time generates a current which flows upward through the entire inductor at an increasing rate. In this way the inductor succeeds (at least momentarily) in keeping the total current from decreasing. This newly generated current again acts as the oscillator feedback current; since it is flowing in the same direction as the tank current, it reinforces it. Thus, the tank current is strengthened or replenished during each half-cycle of operation by autotransformer action.

The tank circuit is considered to be the input circuit, because it drives the control grid. The lower portion of L2 is considered part of the output circuit, because plate current flows through it. Thus, the lower portion of L2 is a part of both the input and output circuits. The Hartley oscillator, of which this circuit is an example, satisfies the general requirement that there be some feedback of energy from the output circuit to the input circuit for an oscillation to sustain itself.

*Obtaining the Intermediate Frequency*—We have seen that two different control grids act as individual throttle valves on the plate-current electron stream which passes through the tube. The oscillations of electrons in the two tank circuits driving these grids are occurring at different frequencies. Both circuits are tuned by turning the familiar tuning dial on the front of the radio. The circuit components are chosen so that the oscillator tank which drives grid number 1 (the lower grid) will always oscillate at a frequency which is 455 kc higher (faster) than that of the antenna current being received. This antenna current, of course, supports the RF tank current which drives the second control grid (grid number 3).

The plate current through the tube will obviously fluctuate at each one of the two basic frequencies; however, it will also fluctuate at many other frequencies which *depend* on these frequencies. Most important are the sum of the two basic frequencies and the difference between them (455 kc). In addition, it will fluctuate at a frequency which is twice their sum, twice their difference, three times their sum or difference, etc.

We are interested in only one of these many new frequencies— the difference frequency of 455 kc—since we have already chosen this as the intermediate frequency, or IF, of our radio. The advantage in using a single or fixed IF is that each of the tuned circuits (normally 4) in the IF stage can be tuned to this one frequency and thereafter will require little or no attention.

Since the plate-tank circuit is tuned to the IF frequency, the pulsations in plate current which occurs 455,000 times each second will very quickly excite an oscillation in the tank. This oscillating plate-tank current has been shown in dotted blue. Fig. 1-8 depicts an instantaneous set of conditions when the electrons of the plate-tank current are moving upward through the primary winding of T1, thereby making the upper plate of the tank capacitor negative with respect to the lower plate. At the same instant, a pulsation of plate-current electrons is arriving from the tube and making this upper capacitor plate still more negative with respect to the lower plate. In this manner the pulsations of plate current *reinforce* the oscillation in the tank current. This sequence of events repeats itself 455,000 times every second when the radio is tuned to a station.

The plate-tank current supports another oscillation of electrons in the grid-tank circuit of the next stage. This is accomplished by transformer action between the primary and secondary windings of T1 and will be discussed more fully in a later chapter.

*Screen-Grid Current*—The wires of grids number 2 and 4 constitute a screen grid, which "screens" or isolates the second control grid from the first control grid and from the plate circuit of the tube. The screen grid is connected to the high positive voltage of the power supply; therefore it also attracts electrons from the area around the cathode. Most of these electrons pass through the screen-grid wires and eventually strike the plate. However, some of the electrons passing through the tube will actually strike the screen-grid wires and will exit from the tube as screen-grid current, or screen current. This current has been shown in dotted red up to the point where it rejoins the plate current. Then both currents are shown in solid red as they proceed along the B+ line of the radio to the power supply.

*AVC Current and Voltage*—The final current which flows in the circuit of Figs. 1-7 and 1-8 is the one associated with the function known as "Automatic Volume Control" (AVC). This current and the resulting AVC voltage which exists on the left plate of C1 have been shown in solid green. The AVC voltage acts as a permanent biasing voltage on the second control grid of V1. The means by which it is obtained will be discussed more fully in Chapter 2.

The AVC voltage varies from a low to a high value, but it is always negative. When the strength of the radio signal being received is low, or weak, the antenna current will be weak, and the AVC voltage stored on the lower plate of capacitor C1 will be a low negative voltage.

When the received signal strength is high, or strong, the antenna current will be strong, and the AVC voltage will be a high negative voltage.

A weak AVC voltage will *increase* the gain of the converter stage. A strong AVC voltage will *reduce* the gain of this stage.

## BEAT-FREQUENCY OSCILLATOR

The beat-frequency oscillator, or BFO, is a special example of the heterodyning process by which two voltages of different frequencies are heterodyned to produce a third voltage of a much lower frequency. In the examples previously studied the input carrier signal was amplitude-modulated and that the resultant difference frequency also carried the same intelligence modulation on it.

A beat-frequency oscillator is required when the input carrier signal has been keyed or coded with dots and dashes. This is a special type of modulation known as interrupted continuous-wave (ICW). The signal can be detected in the ordinary sense by a simple diode detector, such as V3 in Fig. 1-9. However, after the detection process is completed, there would be no audio voltages by which the listener could tell that demodulation or detection had occurred. In such a case, the detection process will have been wasted.

When an RF or IF signal which has been keyed or interrupted to form the dots and dashes of the well-known Morse code or similar intelligence reaches a detector circuit, the diode detector will conduct electrons at a constant rate during the periods when dots and dashes occur. During the periods when these pulses are not occurring, it will not conduct. Electrons flowing at a constant rate downward through load resistor R4 will generate a constant or DC voltage for as long as they flow (during each dot and dash, for example) but this flow will not result in an audio voltage in the headphones. Instead, a single surge of current will flow into the headphones (downward) at the start of each pulse, and another surge of current will flow upward through the headphones at the end of each pulse. The beginning and end of each dot and dash will cause a single cycle of "noise" to be heard in the headphones.

## Identification of Components

The following circuit components perform the indicated functions in this simplified BFO circuit:

*Mixer Components*
R1—Cathode biasing resistor for V1.
R2—Screen-grid dropping resistor.
C1—Input-tank capacitor (variable).
C2—Screen-grid filter capacitor.
C3—Plate-tank capacitor.
L1—Input-tank inductor.
L2—Plate-tank and coupling inductor.
*Oscillator Components*
R3—Grid driving and biasing resistor.
C4—Oscillator tank capacitor (variable).
C5—Grid coupling and biasing capacitor.
C6—Oscillator coupling capacitor.
C7—Plate-filter capacitor.
L3—Oscillator tank inductor.
L4—Radio-frequency choke.
V2—Triode oscillator tube.
*Detector Components*
R4—Variable resistor (volume control).

R5—Cathode resistor.
C8—RF filter capacitor.
C9—Additional RF filter capacitor.
C10—Audio coupling capacitor.
L5—Output inductor.
V3—Diode detector.
M1—Output meter for indicating zero beat.
M2—Headphones for listening to code.

## Identification of Currents

There are at least 15 different electron currents working in this BFO circuit; these include:

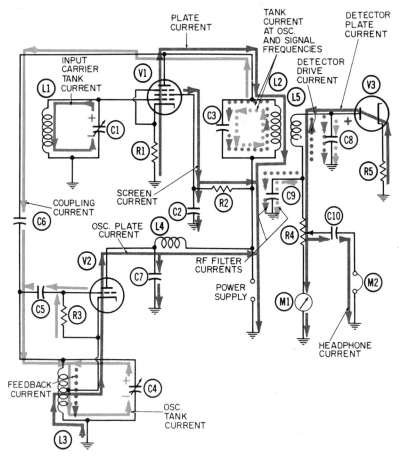

Fig. 1-9. Normal operation of the beat-frequency oscillator circuit.

*Mixer Currents*
1. Input signal tank current (solid blue).
2. Pentode plate current (solid red).
3. Pentode screen current (also in solid red).
4. Screen-grid filter current (also in solid red).
5. Plate-tank current at signal frequency (dotted blue).
6. Plate-tank current at oscillator frequency (dotted green).
*Oscillator Currents*
7. Oscillator tank current (solid green).
8. Oscillator grid driving current (also in solid green).
9. Coupling current to plate tank (also in solid green).
10. Triode plate current (also in solid red).
11. Feedback current in oscillator tank (dotted red).
12. Plate-filter current (also in solid red).
*Detector Currents*
13. Detector drive current (also in dotted red).
14. Detector plate current (also in solid red).
15. RF filter currents (dotted blue and dotted green).

## Details of Operation

Any qualitative analysis of the operation of this circuit should begin with the carrier signal which is received at or delivered to input inductor L1 from a preceding amplifier or the receiver antenna. The signal current (solid blue) oscillates between L1 and C1. (The oscillation is supported by transformer action between L1 and a preceding inductor.) This action and the prior inductor are not shown in Fig. 1-9.

The oscillating tank current alternately makes the control grid of V1 negative and positive. With conditions as depicted in Fig. 1-9, the tank current is flowing downward through L1, thereby removing electrons from the upper plate of C1, making it and the control grid, positive.

The positive control grid encourages, or increases, the flow of plate current through the tube so that a *pulsation* of plate current occurs, one such pulsation occurring for each cycle of the oscillation. Each of these pulsations will support a single cycle of oscillation in the plate tank circuit, consisting of L2 and C3. The oscillation which is generated and supported by these pulsations has been shown in dotted blue.

The values of plate-tank components have been chosen so that they will resonate at approximately the frequency of the incoming carrier signal. Therefore, a natural oscillation will be set up at this frequency whenever a carrier signal is being received. The plate current, which has been shown in red, continues through L2 and enters the positive terminal of the power supply. It is joined at the junction of L2 and R2 by the screen-grid current, also shown in red, which exits from the tube at the screen grid and flows through screen dropping resistor R2. Any pulsations, or surges, which may characterize this screen current as it comes from the tube, will be filtered or bypassed harmlessly to ground through C2. Fig. 1-9 shows a half-cycle of this filter current flowing downward from the lower plate of C2, because a pulsation of electrons has just come from the screen grid. On the next succeeding half-cycle, when no pulsation is occurring, this filter current will flow upward onto the lower plate of C2.

The oscillator circuit which is constructed around triode V2 is a conventional Hartley circuit. The tank circuit, composed of L3 and C4, is tuned by variable capacitor C4. Component values are chosen so that they will resonate at a frequency very close to the frequency of the incoming carrier signal. In this respect, it differs from the circuits previously described, whose purpose was to produce a new frequency (IF) which still falls in what is known as the radio-frequency range. In the beat-frequency oscillator the two input frequencies—the carrier and the local oscillator—produce a difference frequency which is in the low audio range, from a few cycles to a few thousand cycles per second. Furthermore, C4 may be varied so that the difference frequency may be varied over a small range.

The oscillator tank current (solid green) moves continuously between L3 and C4. Fig. 1-9 depicts a moment when the electrons have all moved to the lower plate of the capacitor, thereby making the upper end of the tank positive. This action draws electron current (also shown in green) upward through the grid resistor R3. This makes the top of the resistor and the control grid of V2 positive, and a pulsation of plate current (solid red) will be released to flow through V2. It originates at ground below L3, flows through the lower portion of L3 then through the tube and the radio-frequency choke L5 to the power supply. This current flows intermittently rather than continuously. During that portion of a cycle when it is *increasing* in amount, it induces a feedback current in L3 which is also increasing, but in the opposite direction. This feedback current (dotted red) increases in the downward direction through L3 when the plate current through the lower part is increasing in the upward direction.

Since the tank current is moving downward through L3 at this same time, the feedback current and the tank current are in the appropriate phase with each other so that the tank circuit oscillation will be sustained by the feedback action.

In addition to driving the control grid of V2, this oscillating tank voltage is coupled via C6 to the plate-tank circuit of tube

V1. A single half-cycle of this coupling action is depicted in Fig. 1-9. Since the top of the oscillator tank is positive at this instant, electrons are drawn toward this voltage from the lower plate of C6. This action draws an equal number of electrons onto the upper plate and away from the plate tank of V1. Since the plate tank and the oscillator tank are tuned to almost the same frequency, this coupling action will excite a second oscillation in the plate tank circuit at the oscillator frequency. This oscillating current has been indicated in dotted green.

The coupling action between the oscillator tank and the plate tank could be performed by a straight wire instead of with coupling capacitor C6. The real function of the capacitor is to isolate or block the positive voltage of the power supply from having direct access to ground through L3 and L2.

As we stated in the previous example of a mixer circuit, when two frequencies are mixed, a number of new frequencies are created—namely, the sum and difference, twice the sum and twice the difference, etc. All but one of these are unwanted frequencies, and arrangements must be provided for filtering them all to ground. All of these new frequencies will be inductively coupled between L2 and L5.

The only one of these many frequencies which is wanted is the difference frequency. All of the other frequencies, including the two original frequencies, have an important distinguishing characteristic in common, namely, that they are radio-frequencies and may therefore be easily separated from the difference frequency by simple capacitive filtering. C8 and C9, situated on either side of output inductor L5, provide this filtering.

When the plate of V3 is made positive with respect to its cathode, the diode will conduct electrons. This diode current is shown in solid red. It flows upward from ground through R5, through the diode, downward through L5 and R4, and finally through indicating meter M1.

It is desired that this diode plate current flow *only* in response to the low-frequency "beat note"—which is the difference between the two input frequencies. Neither of these input frequencies, nor any of the other resulting frequencies, will cause the diode to conduct. C8 and C9 both provide a very low impedance path for currents at these frequencies. Fig. 1-9 shows the two original frequencies being filtered through the capacitors to ground. R5 has a low value, but nonetheless any current which flows through the diode must also flow through R5. Consequently, R5 constitutes a load to anyone of these higher frequencies which may attempt to draw current through the diode. Since C8 has lower impedance than R5 to these higher frequencies, each of the higher-frequencies draw current into C8 during its positive half-cycle, and discharge them during its negative half-cycle.

Capacitor C4 can be varied to adjust the oscillator frequency. This varies the difference frequency which the listener hears in the headphones. The difference frequency can be reduced to zero by matching the oscillator and carrier signals. When this is done, the diode conducts no plate current, and milliammeter M1 indicates no current through it. This condition is known as "zero beat," and is the best method for precisely calibrating unknown frequencies against a known frequency. When the two frequencies drift by even a few cycles, the resulting low beat note can be heard by the operator; this enables him to readjust the oscillator frequency to attain the condition of zero beat.

The diode plate current flows only when dots or dashes are being received. It is a pulsating DC rather than a pure DC. The pulsations occur at the so-called difference frequency. Each individual pulsation drives a surge of electron current onto the left-hand plate of capacitor C10, and this action drives an equal amount of electrons downward through the headphone circuit. Between each two successive pulsations, the electron current flows back out of the left hand plate of C10 and downward through R4 and the output meter M1. This action draws electron current upward through the headphone circuit.

In communications receivers it is the usual practice to beat the oscillator frequency against a fixed carrier frequency, rather than against a variable frequency. An example is the 450 kc intermediate frequency or IF generated by the mixer circuit.

### REVIEW QUESTIONS

1. What is the main reason that the heterodyning function is used so widely?

2. Fig. 1-3 indicates plate current pulsations at four frequencies and filter currents at three frequencies. What are the names of these frequencies? Are the three filter currents pulsating DC or true AC?

3. What characteristic of capacitor C2 permits it to "bypass" three of these frequencies, but not to pass

the fourth one? What happens to the fourth one?

4. Explain how a resistor-capacitor combination R5 and C7 filters or "decouples" plate current pulsations, keeping them from entering the power supply. Why is such decoupling desirable?

5. What is the main difference between the pentagrid mixer and pentagrid converter circuits?

6. How is positive or regenerative feedback in Fig. 1-7 developed to replenish oscillator current?

## Chapter 2

# SIGNAL DEMODULATION AND AUTOMATIC CONTROL OF VOLUME

After the IF signal obtained at the mixer output is amplified by the IF amplifier, it must be changed to an audio signal which corresponds to the audio that produced the original modulation at the transmitter. This process is called demodulation or detection. (Actually, detection is a misnomer which stems from the early days of radio when circuits were devised to "detect" or "discover" the presence of a signal from a distant station. Today the term detector is widely used and can be considered as synonymous with demodulator. The term "second detector" is also used when referring to the demodulator stage.)

It is desirable to provide an automatic means of changing the amount of amplification of the signal to compensate for varying signal strengths because of differing propagation characteristics. The AVC voltage and current were discussed in conjunction with the mixer circuit of Figs. 1-7 and 1-8.

The weak audio signal obtained at the demodulator stage requires additional amplification before it is usable. In modern radio receivers all of the foregoing functions—demodulation, automatic control of volume (AVC), and audio amplification—are performed by a single tube.

## DETECTOR, AVC, AND AUDIO AMPLIFIER

The 12AV6 tube (V3) in Figs. 2-1 and 2-2 is capable of performing like two separate and distinct tubes. It is a dual diode-triode tube; independent electron currents can and do flow from the cathode to the diode plates and to the triode plate. In this particular circuit the two diode plates are shown connected together so that they function as if they were a single plate.

## Identification of Components

The components which make up Figs. 2-1 and 2-2, and the portion of the circuit which they function in are as follows:

*Detector Circuit*
R4—Detector load resistor.
R5—Detector load resistor and volume control.
C8—IF filter capacitor.
C9—IF filter capacitor.
T2—(Secondary) Final IF transformer and tank capacitor.
V3—(Diode portion) Detector tube.

*AVC Circuit*
R3—AVC resistor.
C1—AVC storage capacitor.

*Audio Circuit*
R6—Grid driving resistor.
R7—Triode plate-load resistor.
C10—Audio coupling capacitor.
C11—IF filter capacitor.
C12—Coupling capacitor to next stage.
V3—(Triode portion) Audio amplifier tube.

## Identification of Currents

The following separate and distinct electron currents are at work in these three circuits:

*Detector Circuit*
1. Final IF tank current (dotted blue).
2. Rectified current which flows through the diode (solid blue).
3. IF filter current (also in dotted blue).

*AVC Circuit*
4. AVC current (solid green).

*Amplifier Circuit*
5. Audio grid driving current (dotted green).
6. Triode plate current (solid red).
7. IF filter current (dotted blue).

## Detector Operation

The final IF tank current (dotted blue) oscillates continuously between the second winding of T2 and the unnumbered capacitor in parallel with it. The plate-tank current of the preceding IF stage flows up and down through the primary winding of T2 and provides the necessary energy to sustain the current flowing through the secondary winding.

The final tank current alternately makes the top of the tank vary between negative and positive voltage values. Fig. 2-1 depicts an instant when the tank current is flowing upward through the secondary winding and delivering electrons to the upper plate of the tank capacitor, thus making it negative. Fig. 2-2 depicts conditions a half-cycle later when the tank current is flowing downward through the secondary winding, taking electrons away from the upper plate of the capacitor and creating a deficiency of electrons, or, more simply, a positive voltage at the upper plate of the tank capacitor.

These voltage changes (negative to positive and back to negative again) occur 455,000 times each second—the intermediate frequency of your radio. On the half-cycle depicted in Fig. 2-2 the voltage at the top of the tank makes the two diode plates of V3 positive; therefore they attract electrons from the cathode within the tube. These electrons become the so-called diode current, or rectified current, of the circuit. This current is shown in solid blue; it flows through the diode portion of the tube *only* when the diode plates are more positive than the cathode. The complete path of these electrons takes them downward through the secondary winding of T2, and on through resistors R4 and R5 to the common ground connection, from where they have a ready return access to the cathode of the tube. This diode current is a pulsating DC.

The electrons which make up the diode current are prevented from flowing immediately downward through R4 and R5; instead they accumulate on the upper plate of C9, building up a small negative voltage there. This negative voltage is indicated by minus signs in both Figs. 2-1 and 2-2. Even though diode current is not flowing in Fig. 2-1, this negative voltage persists on capacitor C9 and continues to discharge its electrons downward through the resistors. Consequently, although electron current flows intermittently through the diode with 455,000 pulsations occurring each second, it flows continuously downward through the resistors.

*IF Filter Current*—The pulsations in the diode current which are occurring at the intermediate frequency are filtered out be-

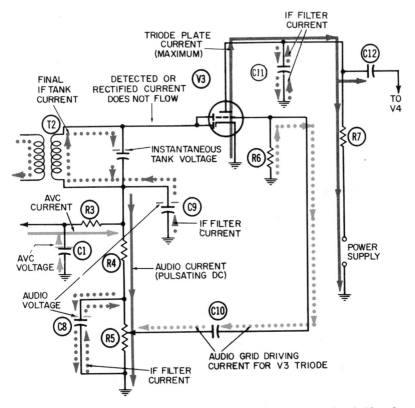

IF FILTER CURRENT

TRIODE PLATE CURRENT (MAXIMUM)

FINAL IF TANK CURRENT

DETECTED OR RECTIFIED CURRENT DOES NOT FLOW

V3

C11

C12

TO V4

T2

INSTANTANEOUS TANK VOLTAGE

R6

R7

AVC CURRENT

R3

C9

IF FILTER CURRENT

C1

AVC VOLTAGE

R4

AUDIO CURRENT (PULSATING DC)

POWER SUPPLY

AUDIO VOLTAGE

C8

R5

C10

AUDIO GRID DRIVING CURRENT FOR V3 TRIODE

IF FILTER CURRENT

Fig. 2-1. Detector, AVC, and audio-amplifier circuit—negative half-cycle of IF tank voltage, positive half-cycle of audio voltage.

tween C9 and the ground. Fig. 2-2 shows a single half-cycle of this current being driven into ground, as a pulsation of diode current flows onto the upper plate of C9. Fig. 2-1 shows the next succeeding half-cycle of filter current flowing back onto the lower plate of C9.

*The Audio Voltage*—The negative voltage which accumulates on the upper plate of C9 is important, since it marks the first appearance of the audio voltage—in other words, the intelligence or the message, you are trying to receive. This voltage can be compared to a pool of negative electrons, with the depth of the pool representing the amount of negative voltage. The depth of the pool does not change significantly during a single cycle of the IF current even though electrons are discharging or "draining" continuously downward through R4 and R5 to ground. This is because the quantity of electrons coming into or going out of the

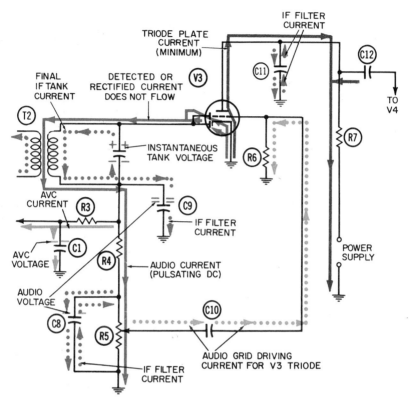

Fig. 2-2. Detector, AVC, and audio-amplifier circuit—positive half-cycle of IF tank voltage, negative half-cycle of audio voltage.

capacitor during a single half-cycle is an insignificant percentage of the quantity which is already stored or accumulated there.

*Modulation*—When the incoming radio wave carries intelligence, such as speech or music, it is said to be *modulated*. The term modulation is often used to describe or refer to this intelligence, and the purpose of a detector (also called demodulator) is to extract this information or modulation from the radio signal current. As mentioned previously, the point at which this extraction process occurs is at the junction of R4 and C9, and the electron pool on the upper plate of C9 marks the first appearance of the *modulation voltage*. This voltage varies at frequencies which are within the range of the human ear—in other words, audio frequencies.

Fig. 2-3 shows a typical modulated waveform. The modulation process which occurs at the transmitter consists of a periodically varying or changing of the strength of the individual cycles of the signal current so that the radio-frequency signal current can be made to "carry" the audio information from the transmitter to the receiver. This carrying process has given rise to the almost universal practice of calling the modulated radio-frequency signal the *carrier*.

The final IF tank current which causes the diode portions of V3 to conduct electrons varies in strength from one cycle to the next in accordance with the modulation pattern. When the tank current is strong, as it is during the modulation peaks shown in Fig. 2-3, larger pulsations of diode current will flow. These larger pulsations deliver more electrons into the pool of electrons accumulated on C9. Since there will be several hundred or thousand individual pulsations of this rectified current flowing through the tube during the period occupied by a single audio modulating cycle, the depth of the electron pool on C9 will increase as a modulation peak approaches.

When the individual cycles of the final IF tank current are reduced in strength by the approach of a modulation trough, the corresponding pulsations of rectified current flowing through the diode portion of V3 will also be reduced. This results in *fewer* electrons being delivered into the storage pool on C9. Thus, more electrons discharge downward through R4 and R5 and flow in during this period, and the negative voltage on C9 *decreases* as the modulation trough approaches.

This process continues as long as a modulated signal is being received, with the result that the negative voltage on C9 (represented by the electrons in storage on the upper plate) increases with each modulation peak and decreases with each modulation trough. In other words, this negative voltage rises and falls at an audio rate, and is therefore, by definition, an audio voltage. This audio voltage first appears on the upper plate of C9.

The current which drains continuously downward through R4 and R5 from this point is driven downward by the amount of this voltage. Consequently, it pulsates at the same audio rate or frequency. This is another of the many possible forms of pulsating DC which exist in a radio during normal operation. It is interesting to note that the electrons which accumulate on C9 arrive there as pulsating DC from the diode plates of tube V3. These pulsations are occurring at the intermediate frequency, or in other words, 455,000 pulsations each second. These same electrons must eventually leave there, also as pulsating DC, but now the pulsations are occurring at whatever audio frequency is being received at the moment—a few hundred or at most a few thousand pulsations each second.

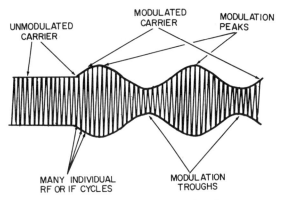

UNMODULATED CARRIER

MODULATED CARRIER

MODULATION PEAKS

MANY INDIVIDUAL RF OR IF CYCLES

MODULATION TROUGHS

Fig. 2-3. Sine-wave representation of carrier-signal current or voltage.

*Ohm's Law*—Since an audio current is flowing downward through R4 and R5, an audio voltage must be developed across these resistors. This is in accordance with Ohm's law, which states that the *current through* any resistor must always be proportional to the voltage across it. The formula for this is:

$$E = I \times R$$

where,

E is the voltage across a resistor in volts,
I is the current through the resistor in amperes,
R is the resistance of the resistor in ohms.

*Coulombs Law*—There is another convenient and simple formula known as Coulomb's law which tells us that the quantity of electrons stored in a capacitor must always be proportional to the voltage across the capacitor. The formula for this is:

$$Q = C \times E$$

where,

Q is the quantity of electrons in storage in coulombs (one coulomb equals about $6 \times 10^{18}$ electrons),
C is the capacitor size in farads,
E is the voltage between the capacitor plates in volts.

The voltage across R4 and R5 which you would compute using Ohm's law would be identical to the amount of voltage stored on the capacitor. This voltage could also be computed using Coulomb's law, if you knew the number of electrons accumulated there. At all lower points on R4 and R5 a proportionately smaller voltage will exist, depending on the distance of the point from the top of R4. Resistor R5 is variable; therefore, almost any proportional value of this audio voltage can be tapped off and coupled to the control grid of the triode portion of V3. R5 serves as the manual volume control and is controlled by the knob on the front panel of the radio.

## Amplifier Operation

*Coupling Action*—During a modulation peak, when the audio current is flowing downward through R5 at its maximum rate, some portion of this current will be diverted onto the left-hand plate of C10; this action will drive other electrons away from the right-hand plate upward to the control grid of the tube and down through grid driving resistor R6 to the common ground. This condition is depicted in dotted green in Fig. 2-2. This would constitute a negative half-cycle of audio voltage, because the voltage developed across R6 by electrons flowing downward through it will be negative at the top and positive at the bottom (since electrons always flow from negative to positive).

During a modulation trough, when the audio current is flowing downward through R5 at its minimum rate, electrons which were previously diverted into the left-hand plate of C10 will now flow back out, and downward through R5 to ground (Fig. 2-1). This action will draw the grid driving current *upward* through R6, and into the right-hand plate of C10. The upward flow of electrons through R6 makes the voltage at the top of this resistor positive; consequently, a modulation trough would lead to a positive half-cycle of operation of the audio amplifier.

*Triode Plate Current*—When the grid voltage is made negative during a modulation peak, the flow of plate current through the triode will be reduced to its minimum value. When the grid voltage is made positive during a modulation trough, this plate current will be increased to its maximum value. This latter condition is depicted in Fig. 2-1.

The triode plate current is another one of the several pulsating direct currents which flow in a radio. After it exits at the plate of the tube it flows to the left-hand plate of C12, where its pulsations are coupled to the control grid of the following stage. The plate current then flows downward through R7 and to the power supply. It eventually will pass through the power supply and be returned to the common ground, from where it has ready return access to the cathode of V3.

It is worth remembering that all tube currents must inevitably be provided with a return path to the cathodes of their respective tubes. Normally, the radio chassis provides these return paths.

*IF Filter Currents*—There are two additional points in Figs. 2-1 and 2-2 where filtering action occurs. Capacitors C8 and

C11 act as filter capacitors for any IF pulsations which were not filtered to ground by C9. We have learned that the electron current which flows downward through R4 and R5 is flowing in pulsations which occur at the audio frequency being demodulated. However, there will inevitably be some small pulsations occurring at the intermediate frequency of 455 kc. These pulsations will divide between C8 and R5 in *inverse proportion* to the impedances offered by these two components. Impedance may be defined as the *opposition to electron* flow which a component offers.

Since C8 is deliberately selected to be large enough to offer *very low impedance* to a current pulsating at the intermediate frequency, most of these pulsations (shown in dotted blue) will be diverted onto the top plate of C8, and each such pulsation will drive an equal number of electrons from the lower plate of C8 to ground. During the periods between each two successive pulsations, electrons will flow off the upper plate of C8 and downward (through R5) to ground, and an equal number will flow up from ground onto the lower plate of C8.

For purposes of analogy, you might assume that 90% of the strength of each IF pulsation which reaches the junction of C9, and R4 will be filtered to ground through C9, and the remaining 10% will enter R4. Also, assume that 90% of the *remaining strength* of each IF pulsation which reaches the junction of capacitor C8 and resistor R5 will be "filtered" to ground through C8, and the remaining 10% will enter R5.

From the foregoing approximations it can be concluded that 99% of the strength of the original IF pulsations is filtered out by C9 and C8, and only 1% flows through R5. This 1%, however, is coupled to the control grid of the triode section of V3 through coupling capacitor C10. Consequently, the plate current stream flowing through this triode, in addition to pulsating at the audio frequency, will also exhibit extremely small pulsations at the basic intermediate frequency. Thus, 90% of the strength of these individual pulsations will be filtered to ground through capacitor C11.

### AVC Operation

In the discussion of the detector circuit operation it was pointed out that the negative voltage pool on the upper plate of C9 would rise and fall at an audio rate and that it represented the first appearance of the audio voltage in a receiver. Since this voltage is never positive, but always negative, it continuously drives electrons downward through R4 and R5. Now examine what happens along the AVC line, which connects to the junction of C9 and R4.

The most important thing you should understand about the AVC line is that it *does not* lead to ground, except through R4 and R5. Therefore none of the diode rectifier current, which is shown in solid blue, can flow to ground through the AVC line.

*AVC Current Flow*—Since the AVC line does not lead to ground, any current which flows through R3 has to be *a two-way current*—a true alternating current. During modulation peaks, when the electron pool on C9 is large, electrons will be driven to the left from C9 into the AVC line, and through large-value AVC resistor R3. This condition has been depicted in Fig. 2-2. It is this current which delivers electrons to the upper plate of C1 and builds up the stored charge which becomes known as the AVC voltage.

During modulation troughs, when the electron pool on C9 is small, the AVC current will flow to the right through the AVC resistor. This action tends to discharge the electrons stored on C1.

From the foregoing, we see that the AVC current is an alternating current which flows through R3 at the audio frequency being demodulated or detected.

*AVC Voltage*—Before a radio is turned on, of course, there is no AVC voltage stored on the upper plate of C1. However, once the detection process begins, electrons will begin accumulating on the upper plate of C1. This accumulation process can result from only one sequence of events, namely, that the AVC current which flows to the left through the AVC resistor R3 during modulation peaks (Fig. 2-2), is larger than the current which flows through the resistor to the right during the modulation troughs depicted in Fig. 2-1.

After several hundred audio cycles have occurred, the AVC voltage on C1 will assume the *average* value of the peak and trough voltages which occur on the upper plate of C9. When this happens, the imbalance between the two half-cycles of AVC current will disappear. In other words, the incoming AVC current of Fig. 2-2 will bring just as many electrons into the storage pool on AVC capacitor C1 as the outgoing current of Fig. 2-1 takes away.

Resistor R3 is a very large resistor—usually 2.2 or 3.3 megohms. C1 is also large—approximately .05 mfd. Therefore the product of these two values ($R \times C$) will give a very long time constant. Using 3.3 megohms, and .05 mfd, the time constant is .165 second; thus, it will require perhaps five or ten times this long to discharge the AVC voltage, once it has accumulated on the upper plate of C1. Obviously, since a single audio cycle completes itself in a small fraction of a second, the AVC voltage cannot discharge itself during a single modulation trough, or even several hundred of them.

Another way of saying this is that the *quantity* of electrons stored on C1 is so great in comparison to the number which flow in or out during a single half of an audio cycle, that the amount of the AVC voltage cannot be changed by a single modulation peak or trough. Still another way of saying this is that the AVC voltage does not "respond" to the audio modulation.

*Signal Fading*—The AVC circuit is provided to protect the listener against undesirable changes in volume as a result of changes in signal strength due to propagation anomalies.

During a signal fade the incoming carrier signal received at the antenna will be significantly reduced in strength. This causes a proportional reduction in all subsequent derivatives of this same current. Therefore, the final IF tank current shown in dotted blue in Figs. 2-1 and 2-2 will be reduced. When this happens, fewer electrons will be drawn across the diode portion of V3 each positive half-cycle, and the audio voltage which appears on the upper plate of C9 will fluctuate between lower values of negative voltage. In other words, both the peak and the trough voltages will be reduced in size when a signal fade—which may persist for several minutes—occurs.

During a fade, a new imbalance is created between the AVC current which comes into C1 during the modulation peaks and which flows away from C1 during the modulation troughs. More electron current will flow away from C1 during a modulation trough than flows into it during a modulation peak. After many cycles have elapsed, this imbalance partially discharges the negative AVC voltage stored on C1, until it eventually again assumes the average value of the peak and trough voltages which are occurring on the upper plate of C9. When it reaches this new average value, the imbalance between incoming and outgoing AVC current again disappears.

A signal fade would ordinarily reduce the audio output of the receiver and require adjustment of the volume control in order to maintain a comfortable sound level. The negative AVC voltage on the upper plate of C1 does this job automatically. Since it is connected to the control grids of the preceding tubes, it acts as a biasing voltage for these tubes. A less negative AVC voltage, which results from a signal fade, will *increase* the gain (amplification) of these tubes and will thereby largely nullify the effect of the signal fade.

*Signal Build-Up*—A signal build-up, which is also caused by propagation anomalies, will increase the strength of the antenna current; this will cause proportionate increases in the strength of each of the subsequent derivatives of that current, including the final IF tank current. Each individual pulsation of detector current through the diode portion of V3 will therefore increase, and the quantities of electrons stored on C9 during each modulation peak and trough will increase. When this occurs, a new imbalance is created between the two alternate half-cycles of AVC current. More current will be driven to the left along the AVC line during modulation peaks than will flow to the right during modulation troughs. This has the effect, after hundreds of audio cycles, of delivering more electrons into storage on C1, than are taken away so that it recharges C1 to a more negative voltage. This imbalance will persist until the AVC voltage again equals the *average* value of the peak and trough voltages appearing on C9.

A signal build would normally increase the output of the receiver, again requiring adjustment of the volume control. With an AVC circuit, the more negative AVC voltage biases the preceding tubes more negatively, reducing their gain and partially nullifying the original effect of the signal build.

As long as a radio is turned on and tuned to a station, there will be some electrons in storage on the AVC capacitor; consequently, the control grids of the converter and IF amplifier tubes will always have some negative biasing voltage applied to them. The amount of this voltage will vary directly with the strength of the incoming signal; therefore the gain of the stages preceding the detector will vary inversely with the strength of the incoming signal. The result is that once the audio output level has been chosen by the volume control, the output level will be maintained or adhered to very closely despite fairly wide variations in the incoming signal strength. Automatic volume control is sometimes called *automatic gain control*.

When a radio is tuned so that it is not receiving any station, or when it is turned off completely, the electrons stored on C9 will discharge to ground through R4 and R5 in a fraction of a second. The electrons stored on C1 will also discharge to ground, but they must first flow through the large resistor R3, and then through resistors R4 and R5. This discharging process will therefore require several seconds for completion.

## GENERATION OF POSITIVE AVC VOLTAGES

One of the many significant differences between vacuum-tube receivers and transistor receivers is in the generation and application of voltages for the automatic control of receiver volume (AVC), or gain (AGC).

With vacuum-tube amplifier stages, gain is most readily varied and controlled by controlling the grid-cathode voltage relationship. A decrease in the negative grid-to-cathode voltage will increase the gain of a vacuum-tube amplifier. A conventional diode rectifier may generate either a negative or a positive voltage, depending on whether the output is taken from the plate or the cathode. In either case, this voltage will vary proportionately with the variations in carrier signal strength.

A positive control voltage, which becomes *more* positive as carrier signal strength increases, cannot be used for automatic gain control in a vacuum-tube stage, because a more positive voltage applied to a control grid will increase rather than decrease the gain of the stage. However, a negative control voltage which becomes more negative as signal strength increases can be used for AVC, since it decreases the gain of a tube amplifier stage. This is the essence of the AVC action in vacuum-tube receivers.

The foregoing restriction does not apply to PNP transistor amplifier stages. Because of the directions of electron flow through a PNP transistor, a positive control voltage, which becomes more positive as carrier strength increases, can be used for AVC purposes. An increase in the positive biasing voltage applied to the base of a PNP transistor will *decrease* the current through the transistor, thereby decreasing the gain of the stage.

### Identification of Components

In the circuit of Figs. 2-4, 2-5, and 2-6, the following components perform the indicated functions:

R1—Emitter biasing resistor.
R2—Base biasing resistor.
R3—First IF filter resistor.
R4—Variable resistor used as volume control.
R5—AVC resistor.
C1—Collector tank capacitor.
C2—First IF filter capacitor.
C3—Second IF filter capacitor.
C4—AVC capacitor.
L1—Primary winding of first IF transformer.
L2—Secondary winding of the same transformer.
L3—Collector tank inductor (primary of IF output transformer).
L4—Secondary of IF output transformer.
X1—PNP transistor.
M1—Detector diode.
M2—Battery power supply.

## Identification of Currents

The electron currents listed in the following flow during normal operation of this circuit. The reader is again reminded that his best chance for understanding how a particular circuit operates is to be able to visualize the various electron currents in motion, and to relate the movements of each current to its neighbor. The student can properly claim that he understands how a circuit operates only when each current has (1) been properly identified, (2) its complete path through the circuit traced out, (3) the action which makes it flow understood, and (4) the job it does visualized.

The following 10 electron currents are at work in the circuit of Figs. 2-4, 2-5, and 2-6:

1. Four IF currents (all in solid blue).
2. Base-emitter current (solid green).
3. Collector-emitter current (solid red).
4. Diode current (dotted red).
5. AVC current (also in dotted red).
6. Voltage-divider current (also in dotted red).

## Details of Operation

In a transistor, electron flow between the collector and emitter is always *against* the direction the arrow of the symbol points. Likewise, electron current from base to emitter must also flow against the direction of the emitter arrow. Figs. 2-4, 2-5, and 2-6 all show these two transistor currents flowing against the emitter arrow.

Two important conditions must be fulfilled for a PNP transistor to conduct these electron currents. These conditions are: (1) the base must be negative with respect to the emitter, and (2) the collector must be negative with respect to both the base and the emitter.

These conditions are fulfilled in transistor X1 by connecting both the collector and the base to the negative terminal of biasing battery M2. Since the emitter is connected to ground (through resistor R1), the negative bias voltage will tend to drive electron current from the base and from the collector into the emitter and through R1 to ground. These currents are appropriately indicated in Figs. 2-4, 2-5, and 2-6.

The intrinsic voltage difference which exists between the base and the emitter at any instant is the most important factor in determining the amounts of these two currents which will flow. To understand what causes this voltage difference to exist or to vary, consider (initially) the movements of three separate electron currents. These currents are:

1. The voltage-divider current (dotted red).
2. The base-emitter current (solid green).
3. The collector-emitter current (solid red).

When this circuit is at rest, meaning when no currents are flowing and when the biasing power supply is disconnected, the three terminals of the transistor will be at ground or zero voltage, since they are all connected to ground through various combinations of resistors and inductors. However, when power is applied to the transistor, the three previously mentioned currents begin to flow; each contributes a substantial change in the voltage or voltages which exist at one or more of the electrodes. It is absolutely necessary to recognize and understand the voltage changes which occur at each terminal. In order to do this, each of the currents which are associated with these voltages must be visualized.

The voltage-divider current, shown in dotted red, is the simplest one of the three to understand, since it does not flow through the transistor. This electron current leaves the negative terminal of the battery, flows to the left through R2, then down, and to the right, and upward through R5 and downward through R4 to ground. Each point along this path is progressively less negative than any point preceding it.

The base-emitter current, shown in solid green, is also driven by the battery. It flows to the left through R2, upward through L2, and into the base of the transistor and out through the emitter, then downward through emitter resistor R1 to ground. Like the preceding current, each point along this path is progressively less negative than any point preceding it. Therefore the emitter is *more* negative than ground because of the current flow through R1, but it is *less* negative than the base, because there is a small amount of resistance between the base and the emitter of the transistor.

The collector-emitter current is also driven by the negative power-supply voltage (although it is regulated or controlled by the amount of current flowing from base to emitter). This current, which is commonly called the "collector" current, flows from the negative terminal of the battery upward through L3, then through the transistor from collector to emitter, and downward through R1 to ground. In flowing through R1, this current develops an additional component of negative voltage across R1, which alters or modifies the biasing conditions existing between the base and the emitter.

In the absence of a received carrier signal, these three currents will very quickly stabilize at "equilibrium" values. Each one will exert its own particular effect on the biasing voltages of the transistor, and each current will become a pure DC.

When a carrier signal is being received, all biasing conditions and all currents are changed. The carrier signal is shown in solid blue, and in Fig. 2-4 it is flowing upward through inductor L1. The applied emf which causes this upward flow has been indicated by a blue plus sign at the top of L1. The resulting induced current in L2 is also shown in solid blue, and flows downward. The "back emf" or "counter-emf" associated with this current is indicated by a blue minus (negative) sign at the top of L2. It is this induced emf which acts as an additional biasing voltage at the base of the transistor.

In any PNP transistor, such as this one, electrons will flow *from* the base and *into* the emitter. In order for this to happen the base must be more negative than the emitter. The base-emitter current, shown in solid green, contributes a small amount

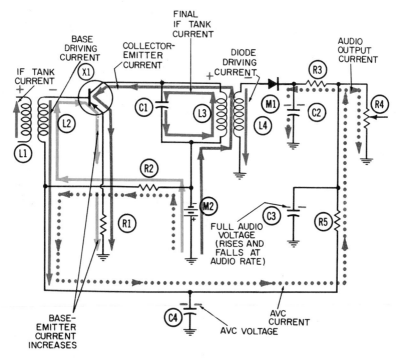

Fig. 2-4. Transistorized IF amplifier, detector, and AVC circuit— negative half-cycle of IF.

of this voltage difference. A much larger component of this voltage difference is contributed by the negative voltage induced at the top of L2 during any negative half-cycle, such as that depicted in Fig. 2-4. Thus the amount of electron flow between base and emitter is greatly increased during a negative half-cycle. The amount of collector current which flows is greatly influenced and regulated by the amount of base-emitter current (usually called emitter current) which flows. Thus, the two transistor currents (base-emitter and collector-emitter) are both substantially increased during a negative half-cycle.

During a positive half-cycle of RF or IF, both of the transistor currents are substantially reduced. This comes about initially when the input carrier current (shown in solid blue) induces a positive component of voltage at the top of L2. This positive component is added to the negative voltage existing at the bottom of L2 by virtue of the voltage divider current shown in dotted red. The net result is a reduced value in the negative voltage at the base of the transistor. Since the PNP transistor requires a negative voltage at the base for electrons to flow from the base to the emitter, it should be evident that any reduction

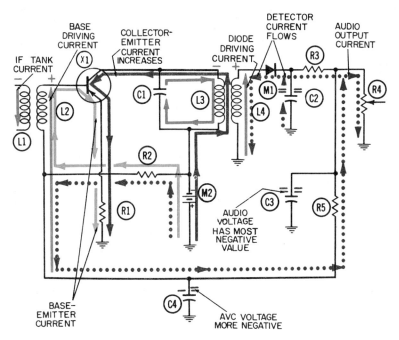

Fig. 2-5. Transistorized IF amplifier, detector, and AVC circuit—
signal strength decreased.

in the negative base voltage will reduce this flow of base-emitter current.

When the base-emitter current is reduced, collector-emitter current is reduced proportionately. Normally, the amount of collector-emitter current which flows is between 10 and 50 times as great as the amount of base-emitter current. It is this property of the transistor which enables it to be used as an amplifier, because a relatively small amount of change in the base-emitter current will cause a substantial amount of change in the collector-emitter current.

Fig. 2-5 shows a positive half-cycle when a relatively weak carrier signal is being received. Fig. 2-6 shows a positive half-cycle when the strong carrier signal is being received. Inspection of Figs. 2-5 and 2-6 will reveal very few differences in current directions or voltage polarities throughout the entire circuit. However, the *amounts* of most currents and voltages will change significantly as we go from a weak signal to a strong signal, or vice versa. It is only by visualizing how these changes occur, and by recognizing their significance, that the AVC action can be understood.

Referring to Fig. 2-5, the pulsations in the collector current as it flows upward through L3 will first shock-excite the tank circuit, C1 and L3, into oscillation, and then each individual pulsation will replenish or sustain a single cycle of this oscillation of electrons in the tank. Of course, the pulsations also occur during the negative half-cycles. In Fig. 2-4 a pulsation of electrons is shown (in solid blue) flowing upward in the tank circuit. In Figs. 2-5 and 2-6 the tank-circuit electrons are returning downward through L3.

A companion current is induced in secondary winding L4 by each primary winding. During the negative half-cycles (Fig. 2-4), this secondary current is shown as flowing downward through L4; during the positive half-cycles (Figs. 2-5 and 2-6), it is flowing upward. The back emf associated with the secondary current has polarities which are indicated by the appropriate signs at the top of L4. The voltage polarities at the top of L4 determine whether or not diode M1 will conduct electrons. When the top of L4 is positive, as it is during positive half-cycles of RF (or IF), M1 will conduct from right to left. This is the normal flow direction for a solid-state rectifier from cathode to anode. This diode current is shown in dotted red. These electrons are drawn initially out of the upper plate of filter capacitor C2, and flow through the diode as indicated, then downward through L4 to ground.

When no carrier signal is present, the upper plate of C2 will charge to a value of negative voltage that is determined by the voltage divider current shown in dotted red. This current flows continuously from the negative battery terminal through R1, R5, and R4, in that order, to ground. The amount of the initial voltage on C2 can be calculated by simple arithmetic using Ohm's law.

During the weak-signal positive half-cycles of Fig. 2-5, when the diode anode is only slightly positive, a small quantity of electrons are drawn out of this "electron pool" on C2 and flow through the diode. This action reduces the negative voltage on C2 so that it becomes less negative than the voltage at the right-hand end of R3. Consequently, electrons will flow from right to left through R3 to equalize this voltage imbalance. Initially, these electrons come from the upper plate of C3, also making the voltage stored there less negative by a small amount.

During the strong-signal positive half-cycles of Fig. 2-6, when the diode anode is made very positive by the induced voltage at the top of L4, a larger quantity of electrons are drawn out of the electron pool on C2 and flow through the diode. This action substantially reduces the negative voltage on C2 so that a greater amount of electrons must flow from right to left through R3 to equalize the voltage imbalance. These electrons come from the upper plate of filter capacitor C3, reducing the negative voltage stored there by a significant amount.

There are three separate and distinct time periods which must be considered when we try to analyze the manner in which an AVC circuit operates. These time periods are as follows:

1. The time required for a single cycle of RF or IF to complete itself—one or two millionths of a second (microseconds, in other words).
2. The time required for a single cycle of audio-frequency to complete itself—a few thousandths of a second (milliseconds, in other words). This time period is several orders of magnitude longer than one that is measured in microseconds.
3. The time required for a signal fade or a signal build to occur, due to atmospheric or propagation anomalies. This will require several seconds or even several minutes to occur. This time period is obviously many orders of magnitude longer than one that is measured in milliseconds.

There are three important resistor-capacitor filter combinations in this circuit, each one of which is designed to respond to a current/voltage action occurring in a different one of these three time periods. These RC filter combinations are as follows:

1. R3 and C2, which respond only to RF or IF.
2. R4 and C3, which respond only to audio frequencies.

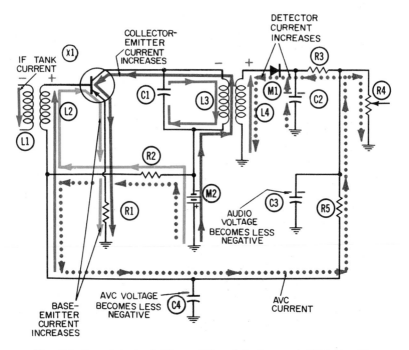

**Fig. 2-6. Transistorized IF amplifier, detector, and AVC circuit— signal strength increased.**

3. R5 and C4, which respond only to sustained changes in received signal strength.

It is evident in Figs. 2-4, 2-5, and 2-6 that negative voltages (meaning electrons) are stored on the upper plates of C2, C3, and C4. The voltage level on C2 rises and falls at the intermediate frequency to which the final amplifier tank is tuned—455,000 cps is a typical example. On positive half-cycles, electrons are drawn out of this capacitor, and an equal number flow up from ground and onto the lower plate of C2. On negative half-cycles, electrons flow downward onto C2 from R3, recharging C2 and driving an equal number of electrons from the lower plate of C2 back into ground. The electron current which flows between the lower plate of C2 and ground is the principal component of IF filter current. (A lesser component which has not been shown will flow between the lower plate of C3 and ground.)

The voltage level on C3 rises and falls at an audio rate. This voltage marks the first appearance of the audio voltage in the receiver system. Fig. 2-7 shows typical waveforms which relate an IF carrier signal to the audio intelligence which it carries. During modulation troughs, the carrier pulsations are relatively weak, and each pulsation will cause only a small number of electrons to flow through the diode on the positive half-cycles. Consequently, the electron pool (negative voltage) on C2 is not depleted as much, and the electron pool on C3, which replenishes the one on C2 will also be depleted only slightly during a modulation trough.

The modulation trough is characterized by a succession of weak positive half-cycles. The modulation peak, on the other hand, is characterized by a succession of strong positive half-cycles. Since large numbers of electrons flow through diode M1 during each strong positive half-cycle, and since these electrons

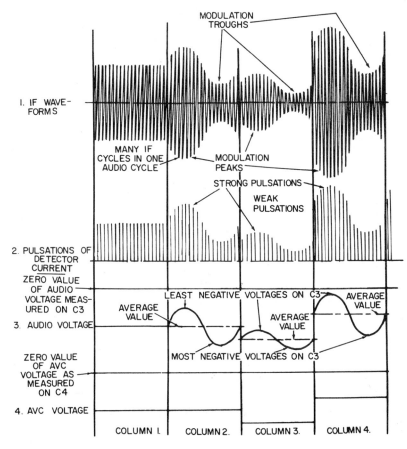

Fig. 2-7. Voltage waveforms at four significant points under four different operating conditions of the circuit in Figs. 2-4, 2-5, and 2-6.

must eventually be supplied from the electron pool on C3, it follows that the negative voltage on C3 is reduced *more* during a succession of strong positive half-cycles than it is during a succession of weak positive half-cycles. Therefore, the voltage on the upper plate of C3 is *less* negative during modulation peaks, and *more* negative during modulation troughs.

The negative voltage stored on C4 does not change with each modulation peak and trough. This voltage will remain constant as long as the average signal strength being received is constant. If this signal strength fades out or builds up due to propagation anomalies, the voltage on C4 will change proportionately, and affect the transistor biasing conditions. Thus, the amplification provided by the transistor is varied. Consider how this voltage change on C4 can be brought about.

First, consider a signal fade. The waveforms of column 3 in Fig. 2-7 indicate that a signal fade is characterized by a long succession of weakened IF cycles so that the modulation peaks as well as the troughs are reduced in strength. Consequently, during the entire period of a signal fade, fewer electrons must be drawn away from C3 to replenish the current which flows through M1. Therefore the *average* voltage on C3 remains at a fairly high negative value.

The negative voltage on C4, which is the AVC voltage, always assumes the average value of the peak and trough voltages which are occurring on C3 (after allowing for the steady component of voltage developed across R5 by the continuous flow of voltage divider current).

Now consider a signal "build." The waveforms of column 4 in Fig. 2-7 indicate that a signal build is characterized by a long succession of strengthened IF pulses. The modulation peaks and troughs are both stronger, placing greater demand for electrons on the negative voltages stored on C2 and C3. The end result of a signal build is that the *average* voltage on C3 will be considerably *less* negative than it is during a signal fade.

During a signal build, the AVC voltage stored on the upper plate of capacitor C5, also becomes less negative. Since the base of the transistor is connected directly to this point, the amount of base-emitter current through the transistor will be *reduced*, and the total amplification which the transistor can provide will also be reduced. This decrease in amplification nullifies or compensates for the adverse effects of the signal build.

During the signal fade previously discussed, the AVC voltage on C4 is more negative than it is during a signal build. This serves as a biasing voltage at the base of the transistor and *increases* the amount of base-emitter current which will flow during any positive half-cycles. This increases the amplification which the transistor provides, and thereby nullifies or compensates for the loss in signal strength due to the signal fade.

Whenever we consider the response of an RC filter circuit, we must inevitably look at the time-constant relationship between each filter and the frequency of the current or currents under discussion. The time-constant formula states that time (in seconds) is equal to the product of the resistance (in ohms) and the capacitance (in farads). The time computed by this formula is called the time-constant of the combination.

It will be instructive to look at the time-constant values for these RC filter combinations using component values taken from a typical transistor radio.

These component values are: R3, 510Ω; C2, 0.01 mfd; R4, 5,000Ω; C3, 0.01 mfd; R5, 39,000Ω and C4, 6 mfd.

The time-constant values of each of these filters is computed as follows:

$$T1 = R3 \times C2$$
$$= 510 \times .01 \times 10^{-6}$$
$$= 5.1 \times 10^{-6} \text{ seconds}$$
$$= 5.1 \text{ microseconds.}$$

$$T2 = R4 \times C3$$
$$= 5,000 \times .01 \times 10^{-6}$$
$$= 50 \times 10^{-6} \text{ seconds}$$
$$= 50 \text{ microseconds or } 1/20 \text{ millisecond.}$$

$$T3 = R5 \times C4$$
$$= 39,000 \times 6 \times 10^{-6}$$
$$= 234,000 \times 10^{-6} \text{ seconds}$$
$$= 234 \text{ milliseconds.}$$

The fundamental requirements which are placed on each of the RC filters is that each time-constant value shall be long when compared to the time for one cycle of one frequency range but that it be short when compared to all of the *lower* frequency ranges. By definition, a time constant is considered to be a long time constant when its value is five to ten times longer than the time duration of one cycle. Under the terms of this definition, time T1 is short when compared to a single cycle of IF (455 kc), which requires more than 2 microseconds of time; but it is long when compared to an audio cycle.

Time T2 is short when compared to the time duration of a single cycle of audio frequency. The entertainment spectrum of audio frequencies ranges from perhaps 50 to 2,000 cycles per second. A twentieth of a millisecond is ten times as short as a half of a millisecond. Also, time T2 is much longer than the time duration of a single cycle of IF (2 microseconds). It is this long-time–constant relationship that enables R4 and C3 to reproduce the audio modulation which is carried by the RF and the IF signal.

Time T3, being nearly a quarter of a second in duration, is obviously long to even the longest audio cycle. Therefore, the AVC filter composed of R5 and C4 does not respond to the modulation (audio voltage) which appears on the upper plate of C3. Time T3 is short however when compared to any of the atmospheric or propagation anomalies which can cause signal fades or builds. These anomalies may last for several seconds or many minutes.

It was stated previously that a PNP transistor amplifier requires a positive AVC voltage and that an NPN amplifier would require a negative AVC voltage. It is evident from line 4 of Fig. 2-7 that the AVC voltage is negative at all times. This is a seeming inconsistency, but one which is explainable by our facility for using specialized meanings for simple words (and frequently without adequate clarification). In this example, what we mean is that a carrier signal must generate an AVC voltage which becomes more positive as the signal strength increases, and *more* negative as the signal strength decreases. Columns 3 and 4 in Fig. 2-7 clearly show this phenomenon.

Both the audio voltage generated on C3 and the AVC voltage generated on C4 are negative at all times. This is due to the action of the voltage-divider current, shown in dotted red, which places all points on its flow path at particular values of negative voltage, each point being at a less negative value than any upstream point, and at a more negative value than any *downstream* point. Both the audio and AVC voltages must fluctuate around their initial negative voltage values.

On a modulation peak, the audio voltage on C3 must become less negative, and during a modulation trough, it must become more negative. These relative values are indicated in line 3 of Fig. 2-7.

The AVC voltage on C4 always assumes or "follows" the average value of the audio voltage on C3. The student should assure himself that he understands how this averaging action takes place. This action would be somewhat easier to explain if the voltage-divider current could somehow be eliminated from the circuit. If R2 were simply removed from the circuit, this voltage-divider current could not flow. Then, the audio voltage on C3 would be positive instead of negative. Each modulation peak would drain more electrons away from C3 to flow through the diode, making the C3 voltage more positive. During each modulation trough, electrons would be drawn upward from ground through resistor R4 and they would reduce this positive voltage somewhat, but not completely.

The AVC voltage on C4 would eventually charge to the average value of these peak and trough voltages on C3. This AVC voltage would be a true positive voltage, since it would be the average value of two other voltages, both of them positive. During each modulation peak, electrons would flow through AVC resistor R5 from C4 to C3, trying to equalize the two different positive voltages. (C3 has the higher positive voltage during the modulation peaks.)

During each modulation trough, electrons would flow from C3 to C4, through R5, again trying to equalize the two different positive voltages. (C4 has the higher positive voltage during the modulation troughs.)

From this we can see that an electron current which may be appropriately labeled as the "AVC current" flows back and forth through R5, always flowing from the point of lower positive voltage to the point of higher positive voltage. Since this current must flow back and forth with each modulation peak and trough voltage occurring on C3, it becomes apparent that the AVC current through R5 flows at the audio frequency being detected or demodulated.

Next, it is appropriate to ask why the voltage stored on the upper plate of C4 does not change with each inflow and outflow of AVC current from or to C3. Why does the AVC voltage on C4 not change or vary in accordance with the changes in amplitude because of the modulation?

This question can always be answered on a mathematical basis by asserting that the RC combination of R5 and C4 is a "long-time–constant" to audio frequencies, and will therefore not respond to modulation. Such a statement is true and unarguable. The physical significance of this statement can only be understood if we consider the *quantities* of electrons which are involved in this current movement, and also the quantity of electrons (or positive ions) which are stored on C4 and which constitute what we know as the AVC voltage.

C4 is a 6-mfd capacitor, which means that it is 600 times larger than C3 (.01 mfd). When these two capacitors are charged to the same value of positive voltage, C4 must, of necessity have 600 times as many positive ions stored on its upper plate as are stored on the upper plate of C3. This is an arithmetical relationship which is covered by the formula known as Coulomb's law. This law states that the voltage across any capacitor is proportional to the quantity of negative electrons (or positive ions) stored in the capacitor. This formula is usually written as:

$$Q = C \times E$$

where,

Q is the quantity of electrons (or ions) in storage expressed in coulombs (one coulomb equals $6 \times 10^{18}$ electrons or ions),
C is the size of the capacitor in farads,
E is in the voltage across the capacitor in volts.

From this relationship one can see that if two capacitors of different sizes are charged to the same voltage, then the larger capacitor will require a larger amount of charge (electrons or ions) than the smaller one.

Again reverting to our hypothetical example, we can see that the inflow of electrons from the AVC current to C3 will reduce its positive voltage, and the outflow of AVC current electrons will increase its positive voltage. The voltage on C4, however, remains virtually unchanged when these same quantities of electrons flow out and in, respectively. This is because C4 is 600 times larger than C3. According to Coulomb's law, a quantity of electrons which will change the voltage on C3 by one volt will change the voltage on C4 by only 1/600th of a volt. The peak value of these pulsations will occur during the modulation peaks and the minimum value during modulation troughs.

## REVIEW QUESTIONS

1. At what point in Figs. 2-1 and 2-2 does the "demodulated" audio voltage make its first identifiable appearance?

2. In Fig. 2-2, what causes the RF filter current to flow away from the lower plate of C9? In Fig. 2-1, what causes this current to flow upward?

3. During a modulation peak, will the instantaneous audio voltage on the upper plate of C9 (Fig. 2-1) become more negative or less negative than during a modulation trough?

4. Describe how an audio driving voltage is developed across grid resistor R6 in Fig. 2-1.

5. In a typical broadcast receiver using AVC or AGC, RC filter circuits will be found which exhibit "time constant values" making them suitable for use in any one of three different frequency or time domains. Name these three time domains.

6. What is the frequency of the AVC current which is shown in solid green in Figs. 2-1 and 2-2? Is this a pulsating DC or a true alternating current? When this receiver is turned off, what happens to the electrons which are stored in C1 and what constitutes the AVC voltage? When the receiver is first turned on, describe the current actions which result in the initial build-up of this AVC voltage.

## Chapter 3

# NOISE-LIMITING PRINCIPLES

In the transmission of a signal between the station and the receiver, noise pulses are often superimposed on the signal. These pulses, which may be caused by atmospheric or man-made conditions, will cause "static" in the output if allowed to pass through the receiver. Most amateur and communications receivers employ circuits for removing these pulses so that they will not appear in the output; however, noise-limiting circuits are seldom employed in "entertainment-type" home receivers. In this chapter, three types of noise limiters—shunt diode, series diode, and dual diode—as well as pentode squelch circuit will be discussed.

## SHUNT-DIODE NOISE LIMITER

Figs. 3-1 and 3-2 show two separate moments during the operation of a simple noise-limiting circuit, which places a diode tube, V1, across the grid input circuit of a conventional pentode audio amplifier, V2. In the absence of an undesirable noise pulse, the diode tube does not conduct; this condition might be labeled as the *normal* mode of operation (Figs. 3-1 and 3-2). When a noise pulse is present, the diode tube conducts, as shown in Fig. 3-3. This conduction biases the control grid of the pentode tube beyond cutoff, cutting off the tube for the duration of the noise pulse.

### Identification of Components

The following circuit components in Fig. 3-1, 3-2, and 3-3 perform the functions indicated:

R1—Variable resistor (volume control).
R2—Variable resistor used as voltage divider to set the noise level.

R3—Cathode-biasing resistor for V2.
C1—Input coupling capacitor.
C2—Coupling and biasing capacitor.
C3—Cathode-bypass capacitor for V2.
L1—Grid-driving and biasing inductor.
V1—Diode tube used as noise limiter.
V2—Pentode tube used as audio amplifier.

## Identification of Currents

Three electron currents will flow in this circuit during normal operation. Two additional currents are introduced during abnormal operation (when a noise pulse is received). These currents, and the colors used to identify them are:

*Normal Operation.*
1. Input audio current (solid blue).
2. Voltage divider current (solid green).
3. Pentode plate current (solid red).
*Abnormal Operation*
4. Noise current (dotted blue).
5. Diode current (dotted green).

Also during abnormal operation, the pentode plate current does *not* flow.

## Details of Operation

Fig. 3-1 shows a negative half-cycle of operation of the noise-limiter circuit when no undesired noise pulse is present. The input audio signal from the demodulator circuit reaches input capacitor C1 and drives an electron current *downward* through R1, producing a negative voltage at the upper end of R1. Each point below the top of R1 will exhibit a lesser negative voltage than that at the top during this negative half-cycle, depending on the distance. Thus, a movement of the potentiometer arm taps off any desired amount of the audio voltage for coupling to V2.

The physical means by which this coupling action is accomplished is indicated in Fig. 3-1. When current is driven downward through R1, it is also driven onto the left-hand plate of C2. This action drives an equal number of electrons out of the right-hand plate of C2 and downward through L1. During this downward motion of electrons through L1, the top of the inductor will be negative in voltage; this is the voltage applied to the grid of V2.

This pentode will be conducting throughout an entire audio cycle, i.e., continuously, during normal operation. This is usually referred to as Class-A operation. During a negative half-cycle,

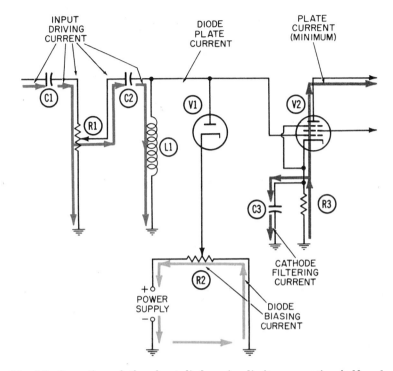

Fig. 3-1. Operation of the shunt-diode noise limiter—negative half-cycle.

such as is shown in Fig. 3-1, the plate current will be reduced to its minimum value.

Fig. 3-2 shows a positive half-cycle during normal operation of this circuit. The input audio current is now being drawn out of the left-hand plate of C1; this action draws electron current upward through R1 and also out of the left-hand plate of C2 and upward through L1. This action places a positive voltage on the control grid of V2 and causes the maximum amount of plate current to flow through the tube.

During both the negative and positive half-cycles of operation shown in these two illustrations a voltage-divider current (shown in solid green) will be flowing continuously through R2 from right to left. This current flows continuously in a counterclockwise direction through R2 and the power supply in ground, then out of ground and back into R2. As the potentiometer arm is moved from right to left, a succession of higher and higher positive voltages will be encountered, and applied to the cathode of V1. This potentiometer arm is used to set the *noise level* at which the circuit operates.

The most important single condition for a diode tube to conduct electron current is that the instantaneous voltage at the diode plate must be more positive than the instantaneous voltage at the cathode. The cathode of V1 is held at a certain value of positive voltage, depending on the position of the potentiometer arm, so that the tube is normally nonconducting. Even the positive half-cycle of audio voltage depicted in Fig. 3-2 is assumed to be insufficiently strong to make the diode plate more positive than this cathode voltage. Consequently, the diode acts as an open circuit during the entire audio cycle. The term "open circuit" is frequently used in this kind of situation and should be considered as synonomous with infinite resistance. Thus, it has no effect on the normal operation of the pentode amplifier input circuit.

Fig. 3-4A shows the RF (or IF) waveform during normal operation. This illustration also shows how the same waveform would be modified and distorted by a typical noise pulse. Noise pulses are characteristically of extremely short time duration and usually of very high amplitude. These pulses may be the result of either natural or artificial interference—lightning bursts, automobile-ignition systems, X-ray equipment, or any one of dozens of other types of industrial electronic equipment.

When the positive half-cycle of even a single cycle of such a noise pulse reaches the plate of V1, it makes this plate more positive than the cathode, and the diode conducts electrons strongly from cathode to plate. The "noise current" which causes this condition is shown being drawn upward through L1 (in dotted blue) in Fig. 3-3 (the resulting diode current is shown in dotted green). This diode current is drawn out of ground below the right-hand end of R2 and flows in a short burst (or a series of short bursts, depending on the number of cycles of noise voltage present) through the diode from cathode to plate. From the diode plate, the current flows onto the right-hand plate of C2, where it accumulates and very quickly forms a "pool" of negative voltage which biases both the diode plate and the pentode control grid negatively. This negative bias at the control grid cuts off the flow of electron current through the pentode until the noise pulse has ended. Thus, no audio occurring during the period of a noise pulse will be reproduced at all. Fig. 3-4B shows the resultant output waveform of V2 when the noise pulses of Fig. 3-4A occur. Here, it can be observed that there is no output at all during the noise pulse.

Since the noise pulse is of such short duration, lasting only for a portion of an audio cycle, or at the most, for just a few audio cycles, the absence is normally not noticeable to the listener. When the noise pulse passes, the electron pool which accumulated on the right-hand plate of C2 will very quickly discharge to ground through L1, and the diode will again be able to conduct electrons on the succeeding positive half-cycles of audio voltage should another noise pulse occur.

The statement appears frequently in the literature on noise-limiting and noise-cancellation circuits that the noise-limiting action punches a hole in the signal. This refers to the fact which is portrayed graphically in Fig. 3-4B, namely, that no audio output signal is delivered while a strong noise pulse is being received.

L1 and C2 act in much the same manner as a long time-constant RC filter. Noise pulses will occur at high frequencies, well above the audio range, so that the electrons in storage on C2 cannot discharge downward through L1 after one noise cycle before the next such cycle occurs.

## SERIES-DIODE NOISE LIMITER

The circuit shown in Figs. 3-5 and 3-6 is another popular noise-cancellation, or noise-limiting circuit. It derives its name from the fact that noise-limiting diode V1 is in series with the audio signal path. During normal operation, the diode conducts continuously, and an output signal is developed across R5 for coupling to the pentode amplifier stage. During abnormal or noise-limiting operation, the diode does not conduct so that no audio signal can be developed across R5 for the duration of the noise pulse.

### Identification of Components

As far as possible, the components in Figs. 3-5, 3-6, and 3-7 have been labeled to coincide with their counterparts in the shunt noise limiter of Fig. 3-1, 3-2, and 3-3. The various components with their functional titles are as follows:

R1—Variable resistor (volume control).
R2—Voltage-dividing resistor for setting the noise level.
R3—Cathode biasing resistor.
R4—Noise-pulse filtering resistor.
R5—Diode load or output resistor.
R6—Grid-driving and grid-return resistor.
C1—Audio storage capacitor.
C2—Blocking and coupling capacitor.
C3—Cathode bypass capacitor.
C4—Coupling and blocking capacitor.
V1—Noise-limiting diode.
V2—Pentode audio-amplifier tube.
V3—Diode detector or demodulator.

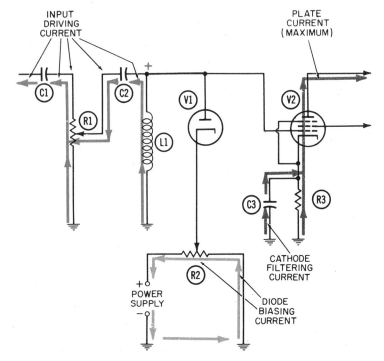

Fig. 3-2. Operation of the shunt-diode noise limiter—positive half-cycle.

## Identification of Currents

The following electron currents will flow in this circuit during normal operation (meaning during conditions when no noise pulse is present):

1. Diode-detector load current, which is also the input audio signal (solid blue).
2. Voltage-divider current (solid green).
3. Noise-pulse current (dotted blue).
4. Diode current (dotted green).
5. Pentode grid-driving current (also in dotted green).
6. Pentode-plate current (solid red).
7. Cathode-filter current (also in solid red).

During abnormal operation, meaning when an unwanted noise pulse is being received, the last four of the currents listed—the diode current, the grid-driving current, the pentode-plate current, and the cathode-filter current—*do not* flow. Since the plate current is invariably being used to deliver an audio signal to the next amplifier stage, or to some output device such as a speaker or

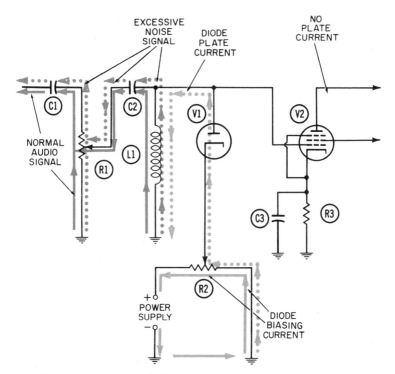

Fig. 3-3. Operation of the shunt-diode noise limiter—excessive
noise pulse being received.

headphones, the cutting off of plate current during a noise pulse
effectively cancels out any other adverse effects of that noise pulse.

### Details of Operation

Fig. 3-5 depicts the current actions which occur during a negative half-cycle of audio operation. The input current (shown
in solid blue) is flowing at an audio frequency and represents the
output of the V3 diode-detector circuit. This current is being
driven downward through R1, causing a flow into the left plate of
C2, and downward through R4. As a result of this downward
movement of electrons, the voltages at the tops of R1 and R4 will
be negative.

The variable tap on R1 enables any desired portion of this negative voltage to be coupled to the diode noise limiter. This variable
feature regulates the amount of electron current which is being
driven into C2 and downward through R4; therefore it regulates
the amount of negative voltage developed at the top of R4 during
this negative half-cycle.

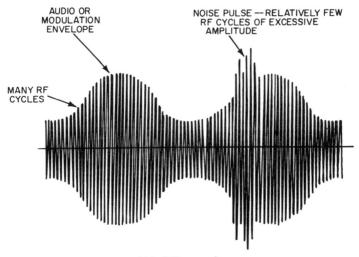

(A) RF waveform.

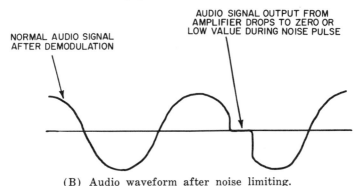

(B) Audio waveform after noise limiting.

Fig. 3-4. Effect of noise pulses on the RF and audio waveform.

V1 is biased by the voltage existing at voltage divider R2 so that it conducts continuously during normal operation. This is accomplished when the voltage divider current through R2 (shown in solid green) flows continuously in the counterclockwise direction, being drawn upward from ground and through R2 to the positive terminal of the power supply. The diode plate is connected to this positive terminal, whereas its cathode is connected to some point of lower positive voltage on R2. Because the plate is more positive than the cathode, the diode current shown in dotted green will also tend to flow continuously. Its complete path begins at the ground connection at the right-hand end of R2. It then flows through part of R2, upward through R5, through the diode, downward through R4, into the positive terminal of the power supply, and through it to ground.

Because of this diode current flow, the voltage at the plate of the diode will be less than the power supply voltage by the amount of current "dropped" or developed across R4 by this same current. Also, during a negative half-cycle of audio, such as is shown in Fig. 3-5, a negative voltage is developed across R4 by the input current (shown in solid blue). The amount of this negative voltage must be subtracted from the positive voltage which exists at the plate because of the biasing actions just described. Therefore, during a negative half-cycle of audio, the positive voltage at the diode plate will be reduced. This will cause a reduction in the amount of diode current (shown in dotted green); this reduction causes a smaller voltage drop to exist across the diode cathode load R5.

The voltage at the top of R5 and the cathode of the diode is positive in polarity at all times. During noise-pulse reception (which is described later) when no diode current flows, the lowest positive voltage which the cathode can attain is reached; this will be the same amount of positive voltage as that which exists at the point on voltage divider R2 where the variable tap is placed. When a small amount of diode current flows during the negative half-cycles, the voltage at the top of R5 will be only slightly more positive than this value. When a large amount of plate current flows during positive half-cycles, the voltage at the top of R5 will be considerably more positive than this value.

Thus, it can be seen that the voltage at the diode cathode and the top of R5 fluctuates between two values of positive voltage, in accordance with the flow of audio-driving current up and down through R4. On negative half-cycles, such as are shown in Fig. 3-5, the diode cathode voltage has its least positive value. On these half-cycles, electron current will flow into the left-hand plate of C4. This action will drive an equal number of electrons downward through grid-driving resistor R6. This is the grid-driving current for V2 (shown in dotted green). The downward flow of current through R6 places a negative voltage on the grid of V2, thereby reducing the plate current through this tube to a minimum value.

During a positive half-cycle of audio, such as that shown in Fig. 3-6, the detector current flowing through V3 and R1 cannot reverse its direction, since a diode is a unidirectional device. However, this current is reduced to a low value on positive half-cycles, causing a reversal of current direction in capacitors C1 and C2 and in resistor R4. During the negative half-cycles of Fig. 3-5, the upper plate of C1 "fills up" with accumulated electrons. During the positive half-cycles of Fig. 3-6, this reservoir becomes depleted.

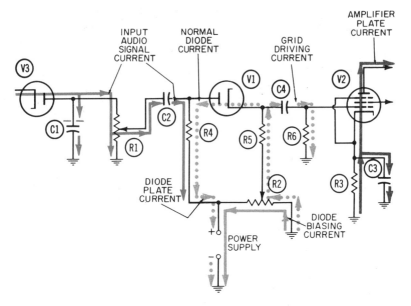

Fig. 3-5. Operation of the series-diode noise limiter—negative half-cycle.

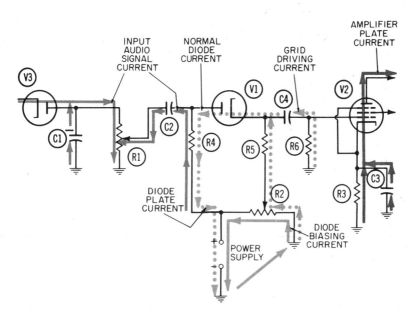

Fig. 3-6. Operation of the series-diode noise limiter—positive half-cycle.

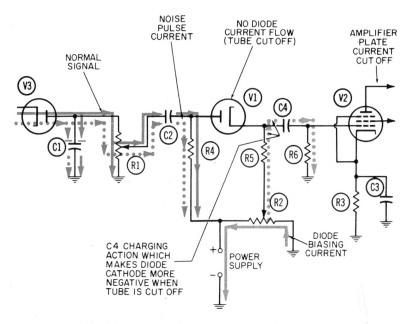

Fig. 3-7. Operation of the series-diode noise limiter—strong
noise pulse being received.

The left-hand plate of C2 acts in a similar manner, accumulating
electrons during negative half-cycles and discharging them back to
R1 during positive half-cycles. In consonance with the charge
and discharge action of C2, the input current (shown in solid blue)
flows downward through R4 during negative half-cycles, and upward through R4 during the positive half-cycles. Thus, during the
positive half-cycles, the voltage developed across R4 by this upward current flow will be positive at the top of R4, thus counter-
acting, to some extent, the negative component of the voltage developed across this same resistor by the continuous downward
flow of current coming through diode V1. Therefore, the diode
plate is made more positive, *increasing* the diode current flow. At
these times (the positive half-cycles) the cathode of V1 will reach
its highest positive voltage; and on these half-cycles, electrons
will be drawn out of the left-hand plate of C4 to supply the increased demand for electrons flowing into the diode. This action
draws an equal number of electrons upward through resistor
R6, and their upward flow (shown in dotted green in Fig. 3-6)
makes the grid of pentode V2 positive, thereby causing the
maximum amount of plate current (shown in solid red) to flow
through V2.

71

## Operation During Noise-Pulse Reception

Fig. 3-4A indicates a typical noise pulse and the manner in which it will distort a normal carrier wave. Resistor R2 acts as a noise-level control in this circuit and will normally be set to a position so that the diode will conduct electrons during the entire range of any audio cycle which might be received. However, when a noise pulse is received, it is desirable that the diode not conduct. Fig. 3-7 shows the additional noise current that flows during receipt of a noise pulse; from this illustration we can see how the noise current cuts off the diode and further results in cutting off audio-amplifier tube V2.

The noise current (shown in dotted blue in Fig. 3-7) is flowing downward through R4. Since the noise signal is by nature much stronger in amplitude than the normal audio signal, this noise current develops a much stronger component of negative voltage at the top of R4. When this negative voltage is large enough, it will exceed the positive voltage which is simultaneously developed between the diode plate and cathode by the voltage-divider current flowing from right to left through R2. When this happens, the diode stops conducting.

When the diode stops conducting, the cathode voltage drops to its lowest positive value; this voltage drop is "coupled" across C4 to grid-driving resistor R6. Translated into terms of current flow, we find electrons flowing *onto* the left-hand plate of C4, driving other electrons *downward* through R6, and making the voltage at the top of R6 negative enough to cut off the electron flow through the pentode amplifier entirely. This portion of the action is identical (except in degree) to that which is depicted in Fig. 3-5 for C4 and R6, when a negative half-cycle of audio occurs.

## DUAL-DIODE NOISE LIMITER

Figs. 3-8 and 3-9 show two separate moments in the operation of a dual-diode noise limiter. Fig. 3-10 shows a typical audio waveform, as distorted by a strong noise pulse. This particular circuit may be used in the audio section of a receiver to protect against a strong negative or positive noise pulse.

### Identification of Components

The circuit of Figs. 3-8 and 3-9 is composed of the following components:

R1—Grid-driving resistor.
R2—Plate-load resistor.

R3—Grid-driving resistor.
R4—Cathode-biasing resistor.
C1—Coupling and blocking capacitor.
C2—Cathode-filter capacitor.
V1—Triode audio amplifier.
V2—Positive limiter diode.
V3—Negative limiter diode.
V4—Triode audio amplifier.
M1—Bias battery (or other voltage source).
M2—Bias battery (or other voltage source).

## Identification of Currents

The following currents are at work in this circuit during normal (no noise pulses) operation:

1. Two grid driving currents (solid blue).
2. Two triode plate currents (solid red).
3. Cathode filter for V4 (dotted red).

During abnormal operation when a noise pulse is present, one of the following additional currents will flow.

4. Positive limiting diode current through V2 (dotted green).
5. Negative limiting diode current through V3 (solid green).

(Both of these currents will flow if the noise pulse has both positive and negative components, but the currents cannot flow simultaneously—they must flow in sequence, or consecutively.)

## Details of Operation

With the two diodes and bias batteries removed from the circuit, it becomes a conventional RC coupled audio amplifier and, in normal operation, acts like one. In Fig. 3-8, if you disregard the current which flows through V2 (dotted green), you see what appears to be a positive half-cycle in the operation of V1. (The term *positive* as applied to a half-cycle of operation is an arbitrary one and can be taken to refer either to the instantaneous grid voltage or the instantaneous plate voltage. It refers to the plate voltage of V1 in this example.)

The grid voltage is negative during this half-cycle, as shown by the downward movement of grid-driving electrons through R1 (solid blue). The negative grid voltage reduces the flow of plate current through V1 and the downward flow of plate current through load resistor R2. Consequently, the voltage at the plate of V1 must become more positive. This rise in plate voltage draws an electron current upward through grid resistor R3 so that the

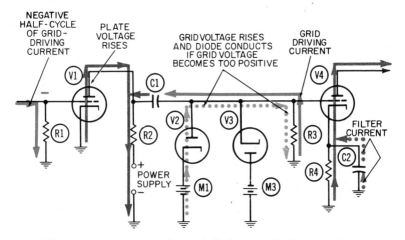

Fig. 3-8. Operation of the dual-diode noise limiter—positive
noise pulse being received.

top of the resistor becomes positive in voltage. (The grid-driving
current in R3 has also been shown in solid blue.)

In Fig. 3-10, that portion of the audio waveform which is above
the center line has been arbitrarily labeled as "positive." That
portion of the waveform which appears sinusoidal in nature is
considered to be within the normal operating limits of the circuit.
The bias battery, or voltage source shown below the cathode of
V2 must be chosen so that it is *equal to or greater than* the voltage
represented by the normal operating limit voltage. When this is

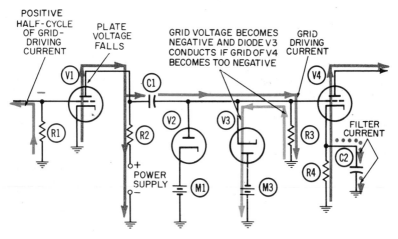

Fig. 3-9. Operation of the dual-diode noise limiter—negative
noise pulse being received.

NVC 1963-1967

Vol 1

page 228

col 3

done, under normal conditions, V2 cannot conduct because the diode plate voltage can never become more positive than the cathode voltage.

When a strong noise pulse having a positive polarity is received, normal conditions are exceeded. The most positive voltage that the plate of V1 can attain is the value of plate-supply voltage provided by the power supply. It will reach this value only if and when the control grid of V1 is made negative enough to cut off the flow of plate current entirely. A strong noise pulse would be the most likely cause of V1 cutting off.

Before the plate of V1 (and the grid of V2) can become this positive, the plate of V2 will become more positive than its cathode, with the result that diode current will flow. This current (shown in dotted green) flows along the path shown from cathode to plate within V2 and downward through R3 to ground. Since it is flowing through R3 in a direction *opposite* to the flow of the grid-driving current, it partially neutralizes the high positive voltage which would otherwise be developed across R3.

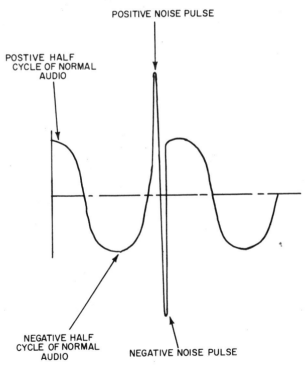

Fig. 3-10. Amplitude relationships between normal audio cycles and unwanted noise pulses.

As the noise pulse increases in strength, it tends to draw more electron current upward through R3; this, in turn, makes the diode plate even more positive and thereby increases the amount of diode current. Thus, a larger amount of diode current is available to flow downward through R3, tending to neutralize any increased positive voltage at the grid of V4 due to a stronger noise pulse.

Fig. 3-9 shows what might be called a negative half-cycle in the operation of the circuit (the term "negative" being used to describe the direction in which the plate voltage of V1 changes). The lowest point on the audio sine wave of Fig. 3-10 is well within the operating limits of the circuit; no current will flow through diode V3. The grid of V1 is made positive during this half-cycle as a result of current being drawn *upward* through R1. This releases a large pulsation of plate current into tube V1, and by virtue of their downward flow through load resistor R2, the plate voltage is lowered. This drop in voltage at the plate of V1 drives electron current downward through grid resistor R3, making the grid of V4 negative.

If a strong negative noise pulse is being received, the voltage at the grid of V1 will be made excessively positive, probably causing "saturation" current to flow in V1. This would lower the plate voltage of V1 to its lowest possible value, and thus, in turn, drive the grid of V4 so negative that it would probably be cut off. This is an undesirable condition, and one which exceeds the normal operating limits of the circuit. The bias voltage below the plate of diode V3 has a value which is so chosen as to be considerably less than this value of cutoff grid voltage. Consequently, before the grid voltage can reach such a negative voltage, the cathode of V3 will become more negative than its plate, and V3 will conduct an overload, or limiting current (shown in green). It flows upward through R3 and downward from the cathode to the plate of diode V3.

Since it flows upward through R3 while the grid-driving current is flowing downward through the same resistor, it partially offsets, or neutralizes, the large negative voltage which would otherwise exist at the grid as a result of the negative noise pulse. If the noise pulse becomes stronger, the diode conducts more electron current and thus tends to counteract the effects of the noise pulse flowing through R3.

Since both the positive and negative noise pulses cannot be occurring simultaneously (or they would cancel each other out) the two noise limiting diodes cannot conduct at the same moment. A noise pulse may be either positive or negative at any given instant, but not both.

# SQUELCH CIRCUIT

In the reception of certain types of communications, it is necessary for someone to be listening to the receiver at all times, even when no signal is being received. This is done so that when a signal does come in, it will not be missed. A Federal airways ground station guarding several different channels or frequencies on several different receivers, all simultaneously, is a good example of this. There is a certain disagreeable background noise or hissing which comes from a receiver under conditions of no-signal reception. With two or more channels being guarded at the same time, this combination of background noises becomes most unpleasant, often leading even to inattentiveness on the operator's part and ultimate loss in communications.

The squelch circuit is a simple combination of parts which is designed to eliminate this undesirable condition. The squelch circuit is a carrier-operated device, or switch, which turns the audio amplifier off when no carrier signal is being received and turns it on when a carrier signal is present. The switching action uses the negative voltage which is associated with the AVC action to accomplish this function.

Two identical circuit diagrams have been selected to illustrate how this function has been accomplished. Fig. 3-11 shows a typical half-cycle of audio operation when a signal is being received. Fig. 3-12 depicts operating conditions when no signal is being received and the squelch circuit cuts off the amplifier tube.

## Identification of Components

The squelch circuit and the audio amplifier contain the following individual components, with functions as indicated:

R1—Isolating resistor.
R2—Grid-return resistor for squelch tube.
R3—Variable resistor used as Squelch Control.
R4—Load resistor for V1; also serves as grid-driving and grid-return resistor for V2.
R5—Additional grid-return resistor.
R6—Voltage-divider resistor.
R7—Cathode-biasing resistor.
R8—Amplifier-load resistor.
C1—AVC storage capacitor.
C2—Screen-filtering capacitor.
C3—Audio-input coupling capacitor.
C4—Cathode-bypass capacitor.
C5—Output-coupling capacitor.

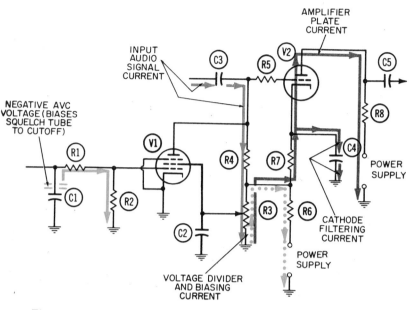

Fig. 3-11. Operation of the squelch circuit—negative half-cycle of audio being received.

V1—Pentode used for squelching purposes.
V2—Triode audio amplifier.

## Identification of Currents

During the normal operation, when a carrier signal is being received, the following electron currents will flow:

1. Current discharge from AVC storage capacitor (solid green).
2. Input audio current (solid blue).
3. Voltage-divider current (dotted green).
4. Amplifier-plate current (solid red).
5. Cathode-filter current (also in solid red).

When no carrier signal is present, the voltage divider current (shown in dotted green) is the only one of the foregoing currents that will flow. However, plate and screen current (both shown in solid red) will then flow in squelch tube V1.

## Details of Operation

When a carrier signal is being received in a typical receiver, it will normally be used, among other things, to generate an AVC voltage. This voltage is stored on a large-value AVC storage capacitor. C1 in Figs. 3-11 and 3-12 provides this function.

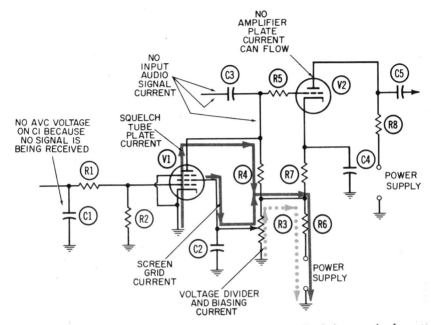

Fig. 3-12. Operation of the squelch circuit—no audio being received.

The AVC voltage is a negative voltage, consisting of an accumulation of electrons in storage on one plate of the capacitor. When the received carrier signal increases in strength, additional electrons are placed in storage on the capacitor, thereby increasing the amount of the negative AVC voltage. When the received carrier signal is reduced in strength, some electrons are given up from storage, thereby reducing the amount of the negative AVC voltage. When no carrier signal is present, all electrons in storage on the AVC capacitor will discharge to ground through R1 and R2 (Fig. 3-12).

None of the circuitry necessary for the generation of the AVC voltage has been shown in Figs. 3-11 and 3-12, nor discussed in this chapter. Refer to Chapter 2 of this book or to an earlier text, *Detector and Rectifier Circuit Actions*, for a full discussion of this circuitry.

The negative voltage stored on the upper plate of C1 causes a continual discharge of electrons through R1 and R2, as shown in Fig. 3-11. This places the grid of squelch tube V1 at a sufficiently negative voltage to cut off the normal flow of plate current through this tube. Thus, whenever a carrier signal is being received, the squelch tube does not conduct. Under these conditions V2 is biased by the voltage divider current (shown in dotted green) as well as by its own cathode-to-plate current (shown in solid red). It is driven by the audio-input signal (shown in solid blue).

The voltage-divider current flows continuously along the path shown, upward through R3 and downward through R6 and into the power supply. Thus, a fixed positive voltage is provided at the junction of these two resistors. It will be noted that both the cathode and the control grid of V2 are returned to this same point, therefore the positive voltage resulting from the flow of voltage divider current biases the cathode and grid of V2 equally. This intrinsic voltage could be almost any value up to full B+, depending on the choice of sizes for R3 and R6.

When plate current flows through V2, it must follow the complete path indicated in solid red in Fig. 3-11. This current originates at ground below R3, and flows upward through R3 before entering cathode resistor R7 and flowing upward through it to the cathode. It then flows through the tube from cathode to plate, downward through R8, and into the power supply, then through it to the common ground where it has ready return access to R3. In flowing upward through R7, an even more positive voltage is created at the cathode. Thus, the cathode is biased positively with respect to control grid, or stated differently the control grid is biased negatively with respect to the cathode—the normal operating condition for an amplifier.

The audio-input current (shown in solid blue) is coupled to the amplifier circuit via C3. Its complete path is, into the left-hand plate of C3, driving an equal number of electrons out of the right-hand plate and downward through R4 and R3 to ground. These two resistors, R4 and R3, consequently serve as grid-driving resistors for V2 in addition to their other functions as a plate-load resistor (R4) for V1 and a biasing resistor (R3) for the screen grid of V1 and the control grid and cathode of V2.

During the negative half-cycle of operation depicted in Fig. 3-11, the control grid of V2 will be made more negative than usual, and the plate current flowing through the tube will be reduced to a low value. Also, at this time, the cathode filter current for V2 will be flowing downward to filter capacitor C4.

During the positive half-cycles of audio operation, the audio current and the cathode-filter current will reverse directions. That is, audio current will be drawn out of C3; this action will, in turn, draw an equal number of electrons upward through R3 and R4 and into the right-hand plate of C3. This action adds a component of positive voltage at the control grid of V2, or, stated differently, it reduces the amount of negative bias existing between the grid and cathode of V2. Thus, more plate current will flow through the tube during the positive half cycles.

## Operation When No Carrier Signal Is Present

Fig. 3-12 depicts the two currents which flow in the squelch circuit when no carrier signal is being received. When there is no carrier signal, there is, of course, no audio signal to be demodulated, and no AVC voltage can be developed from it.

When the negative AVC voltage normally stored on C1 is removed, V1 will begin to conduct. This plate current begins at the ground connection below the cathode, passes through the tube, through R4 and R6, through the power supply to ground.

This downward flow of electron current through R4 makes the upper end of this resistor negative with respect to the lower end. Since the grid of V2 is connected to the upper end of R4, while the cathode of V2 is connected to the lower end of R4, conditions are suitable for restricting or cutting off the flow of plate current through V2. Normally, the amount of plate current through V1 will be of sufficient magnitude that it develops a large enough component of negative voltage across R4 to cut off V2. This, of course, is the basic purpose of a squelch circuit—to prevent the audio amplifier from conducting when no carrier is being received.

The variable tap on squelch control R3 can be used to vary the amount of positive voltage on the screen grid of V1. The squelch control provides a simple means of selecting or rejecting signals of any desired strength or intensity. This feature is particularly attractive for adapting to variable atmospheric phenomena, as well as varying operating conditions or criteria.

### REVIEW QUESTIONS

1. In the circuit of Fig. 3-1, what circuit action determines the bias voltage of diode V1?

2. In this same circuit, what circuit action causes V1 to conduct?

3. When V1 conducts, what effect does it have on the voltage at the control grid of amplifier tube V2 and why?

4. Does this same noise-limiter circuit operate on negative noise pulses, on positive noise pulses, or on both?

5. In the circuit of Fig. 3-5 is the diode normally "conducting" or "cut off"? How does this compare with normal operation of the shunt diode limiter previously discussed? (Normal operation

may be defined as reception of a signal of normal strength, with no noise pulses present.)

6. What is the fundamental difference in the operation of the dual-diode limiter of this chapter as compared to the two single-diode limiters previously discussed? Does this difference make the dual-diode circuit more or less versatile than the single-diode circuits?

7. What is the main reason for using a squelch circuit in a communications receiver?

8. Will squelch tube V1 in Figs. 3-11 and 3-12 be caused to conduct or to be cut off by the existence of an AVC or AGC voltage?

## Chapter 4

# HALF-WAVE POWER SUPPLY

The primary function of a rectifier power-supply circuit in a typical piece of electronic equipment, such as a radio, is to convert the alternating current (AC) which is supplied to homes to direct current (DC). This is a necessary function, because vacuum-tube circuits require the application of fairly high and stable voltages to the tube plates and screens. The purpose of this chapter is to clarify the difference between an alternating current, or voltage, and a direct current, or voltage, and then to show how this direct voltage is achieved with this circuit.

### HALF-WAVE RECTIFIER CIRCUIT

Figs. 4-1 and 4-2 show the two half-cycles of operation in a half-wave rectifier circuit. While a transformer has been employed in this circuit, it is often omitted and the power line is connected (through the switch) directly to the rectifier tube plate. In either case, operation of the circuit is the same.

#### Identification of Components

The components of the power supply circuit shown in Figs. 4-1 and 4-2 and their function are as follows:

R10—Filter resistor.
C14—Filter capacitor.
C15—Filter capacitor.
T4—Power transformer.
V5—Half-wave rectifier tube.

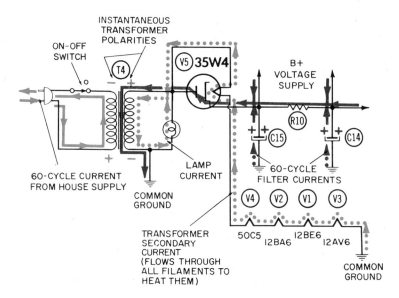

**Fig. 4-1. Operation of a half-wave power supply—positive half cycle.**

In addition, the filament circuits for all tubes in the radio (V1 through V5) are included in Figs. 4-1 and 4-2. Each of these filaments heats the cathode of its respective tube so that the cathodes may emit electrons within the tubes.

### Identification of Currents

There are four separate and distinct electron currents at work in the circuit of Figs. 4-1 and 4-2 during normal operation. These electron currents are:

1. Transformer primary current (solid blue).
2. Transformer secondary current (dotted blue).
3. Rectifier plate current (solid red).
4. 60-cycle filter currents (dotted red).

### Details of Operation

The On-Off switch of the radio is shown in the upper left-hand corner of Figs. 4-1 and 4-2. When this switch is opened, or "Off," the radio is isolated from the house electrical supply, and no electron currents will flow in any of the circuit components. When the switch is closed, or "On," (Figs. 4-1 and 4-2) the house current (solid blue) will flow back and forth through the primary winding of T4.

A half-cycle when the house current is flowing upward through the primary winding of T4 is depicted in Fig. 4-1. The instantaneous voltage polarities across the primary winding are as shown, namely, the upper end of the winding is negative and the lower positive. These are the polarities of the applied voltage, meaning that these voltages are applied from the house supply and, in turn, cause the primary current to flow.

The secondary current is shown as flowing downward through the secondary winding. Associated with this current are the instantaneous polarities of the induced voltage, which are positive on the upper end and negative at the lower end of the secondary. This current also flows through the filaments of the five vacuum tubes, which are connected in series. During the half-cycle represented by Fig. 4-1, this filament current flows to the left through all of the filaments. Each of the filaments is heated by this process very much as the coil of an electric toaster is heated.

During the half-cycle represented by Fig. 4-2, the direction of flow of both the primary and secondary currents is changed. The primary current flows downward, and the secondary current flows upward and to the right through the tube filaments. The voltage polarities across the primary and secondary windings are also reversed during this half-cycle. Since we have assumed the supply current to be conventional 60-cycle, the positive and negative half-cycles shown in these two illustrations are repeated 60 times each second.

### Diode Tube Operation

Referring again to Fig. 4-1, the diode plate current (solid red) is shown flowing from the cathode to the plate of V5. The complete path of this current is from the filter system made up of resistor R10 and capacitors C14 and C15, through V5, and through the secondary winding of the T4 to ground.

In order for a vacuum tube, such as V5, to allow electron current to flow across the open space within the tube, two essential conditions must be met:

1. The cathode must be heated by some external means so that it will emit electrons into the tube. This heating is accomplished by placing the cathode very close to the filament, which is heated by the flow of transformer secondary current described previously. The emission process is analogous to the action that occurs at the surface of boiling water, when very small droplets of water appear to jump free from the surface.
2. The plate of the tube must be at a more positive potential

than the cathode in order to attract the negative electrons across the tube. Since every electron possesses one unit of negative charge, it will be repelled by any negative voltage and attracted by any positive voltage.

In V5 the first of these conditions is fulfilled whenever the On-Off switch is closed. The second condition is fulfilled only during the positive half-cycles depicted in Fig. 4-1. Thus, diode current (solid red) flows only during the positive half-cycles.

It is important to understand the complete diode-current path. All of the plate and screen-grid currents from the four other tubes eventually join together at the junction of R10 and C15 to make up the diode current. This current flows through diode V5 on positive half-cycles only; therefore, it can be described as a pulsating DC. The purpose of the filter system composed of R10, C14, and C15, is to smooth out this pulsating flow of electron current so that the currents flowing from the other tube plates and screen grids will flow smoothly up to the filter circuit.

## The Filter Circuit

R10 and C15 form a simple RC filter circuit, which operates to create a high positive voltage on the upper plate of C15. This high positive voltage is obtained as a result of the departure of many electrons which are drawn into V5. Electrons leave the upper plate of C15 in pulsations (whenever the plate of V5 is more positive than the cathode), creating an electron deficiency on the upper plate of C15. It is this electron deficiency, which is the same thing as a positive voltage, that attracts electrons from the plates and screen grids of other tubes.

As electrons flow in from the other tubes, they would tend to equalize or neutralize the positive voltage on C15. However, other electrons are being drawn into V5 as fast as they are arriving from the other tubes, with the result that a positive voltage remains on the upper plate of C15 as long as the radio is turned on. Thus, we have a situation where electrons continuously flow onto the upper plate of C15, and intermittently flow from this same capacitor and into the diode tube V5.

The amounts of electrons involved in these two current patterns will eventually stabilize and be equal to each other, resulting in a voltage on the upper plate of C15 which is almost as positive as the peak voltage on the upper terminal of the transformer secondary winding.

It is the positive voltage at the upper end of the transformer secondary winding that attracts electrons across V5 during the positive half-cycles. Likewise, it is the resulting positive voltage on the upper plate of C15 that draws electrons from the plates and screen grids of the other tubes. The positive voltage on the upper plate of C15 is a DC voltage, as a result of the filter action which occurs between R10 and C15. These two components form what is known as a long time-constant circuit. This is a mathematical term, but its significance can be explained and understood with the use of some simple arithmetic. When any resistor and capacitor are connected together, they have a time constant, which is determined by the product of the values of the two components. This relationship is expressed by the formula:

$$T = R \times C$$

where,

T is the time constant of the combination in seconds,
R is the resistor value in ohms,
C is the capacitor values in farads.

The time constant of any circuit is considered to be long when it is at least several times longer than the time or period of one cycle of the current which is passing through the combination. Assuming the value of R10 is 680 ohms and C15 is 80 mfd, the time constant of the two components is:

$$
\begin{aligned}
T = R \times C \\
= 680 \times 80 \times 10^{-6} \\
= 54{,}400 \times 10^{-6} \\
= .0544 \text{ second} \\
= \text{approximately } 1/18\text{th of a second.}
\end{aligned}
$$

Since the frequency of the current this filter is trying to handle is 60 cps, the time or *period* of one of these cycles is one sixtieth of a second. Thus, the time constant of the combination of R10 and C15 is more than three times as long as one of these periods.

The positive voltage on the upper plate of C15 can be likened to a pool of positive ions. As more negative electrons are drawn away from this pool and flow through V5, the number of positive ions on C15 will increase by the same amount. Also, as electrons flow into this pool of ions from the plates and screen grids of the other tubes. (Fig. 4-2), the number of positive ions will be reduced accordingly.

Positive ions in concentration represent a positive voltage the amount of which is directly proportional to the number of ions present. The voltage at the cathode of V5 and at the upper plate of C15 in a typical radio will be +125 volts. This voltage does not change significantly from half-cycle to half-cycle, because the quantity of electrons which leave the capacitor on the positive half-cycles is an insignificant percentage of the quantity of positive

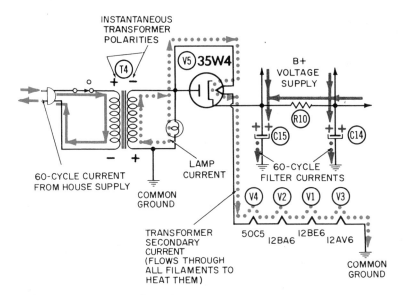

Fig. 4-2. Operation of a half-wave power supply—negative half cycle.

ions already stored there, and the electrons which do leave are replenished during the negative half-cycles.

### Ripple Voltage

All power-supply filter circuits exhibit a *ripple voltage*. The ripple voltage is the minute fluctuations in output voltage that exist as a result of electrons being drawn away from the voltage pool on C15 on the positive half-cycles. In a very long time-constant circuit, this ripple voltage will be an exceedingly small fraction of a volt. In a less sophisticated system, such as the typical radio, it will be much larger. However, if the ripple factor becomes too large, the operation of a radio will be adversely affected, and you will hear a 60-cycle hum along with the regular program.

A filter capacitor, such as C15, operates like a mechanical shock absorber. On each positive half-cycle, such as is depicted in Fig. 4-1, electrons are drawn away from the upper plate of C15 and through V5; an equal number will also be drawn upward from ground onto the lower plate of the capacitor. Likewise, on the negative half-cycles, such as are depicted in Fig. 4-2, V5 is not conducting, but the positive voltage on the upper plate of C15 will continue to draw electrons onto it from the plates and screen grids of all other tubes; this action will drive an equal number of filter current electrons downward from the lower plate of C15 to ground. This filter current has been shown in dotted red in Figs. 4-1 and 4-2.

## Other Tube Currents

The electron currents which flow in and out of C14 are regulated and controlled by the same events which drive the currents in and out of C15, but to a lesser degree. All of the tube currents (plate and screen grid currents) from V1, V2, and V3, plus the screen-grid current from V4, must flow through R10 on their way to the power supply. (The plate of V4 is connected to the junction of C15 and R10.) These currents flow toward V5 because the diode plate is made positive on the positive half-cycles drawing electron current from the upper plates of both C15 and C14. Fig. 4-1 depicts these positive half-cycles, and shows electron current being drawn *out* of the upper plate of capacitor C14, and to the left through R10 to the cathode of the power supply diode V5.

Fig. 4-2 depicts the negative half-cycle operation, when the diode plate is negative, and no electron current crosses V5. During these half-cycles, the positive voltage on the upper plates of C15 and C14 will continue to draw electron current from the plates and screen grid currents of the other four tubes. During this half-cycle, these electron currents will flow *onto* the upper plates of these two capacitors, and will drive filter currents from the lower plates to ground. These flow directions have been indicated by arrows in Fig. 4-2.

### REVIEW QUESTIONS

1. What are the two conditions which must be met in order for a diode to conduct?

2. Describe the electron action (or actions) which keeps the upper plate of capacitor C15 in Fig. 4-1 at a positive voltage.

3. Inasmuch as electrons are drawn away from the upper plate of C15 during a small portion of each cycle, why does the voltage on C15 not change appreciably during each cycle?

4. In Figs. 4-1 and 4-2 electron current shown in solid red is flowing from right to left through resistor R10. What is this current usually called and where does it come from?

5. In the 35W4 tube of this chapter, does the filament heating current shown in solid blue cross the diode tube from cathode to plate?

## Chapter 5

# REGENERATION

Regenerative circuits were widely used in the early days of radio. For example, a regenerative detector was often employed to detect, or demodulate, very weak radio-frequency signals because of its ability to amplify the signal as it was demodulated. Such signals might have been continuous wave (CW) signals used for the transmission of code, or amplitude-modulated (AM) signals carrying voice or entertainment-type information.

## REGENERATIVE DETECTOR

A typical regenerative detector circuit is given in Figs. 5-1, 5-2, and 5-3. Gains in signal strength of 10,000 or 12,000 are common with this type of circuits. In modern entertainment-type equipment, the regenerative detector is seldom encountered; however, it is often employed in small communications-type receivers.

The development of new RF amplification techniques has led to the abandonment of the regenerative detector in entertainment-type equipment. For example, an RF amplifier circuit with a voltage gain, or amplification, of 30 times is not uncommon. Three such stages in series, or cascade, would have an over-all gain of 27,000. While such a circuit would require three tubes instead of one and appear to invite more complexity and cost, it eliminates the inherent disadvantages of the regenerative detector, namely, the need for critical adjustment. A slight misadjustment in a "regen" detector can cause it to go into self-sustained oscillation, even in the absence of a radio-frequency signal.

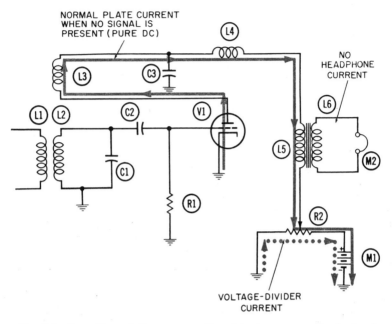

Fig. 5-1. Operation of the regenerative detector—no received signal.

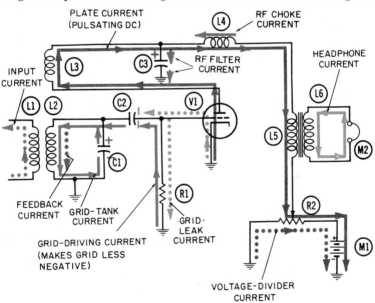

Fig. 5-2. Operation of the regenerative detector—positive
half-cycle of signal.

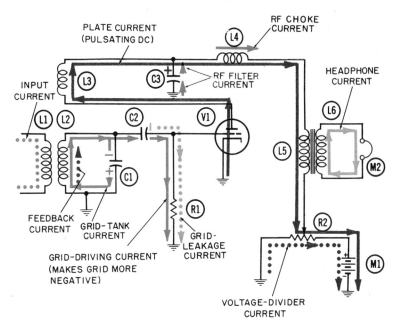

Fig. 5-3. Operation of the regenerative detector—negative
half-cycle of signal.

## Identification of Components

The components which make up the regenerative detector
circuit are shown in Fig. 5-1, 5-2, and 5-3, and their functions are
as follows:

R1—Grid-leak biasing resistor.
R2—Variable resistor used as voltage divider.
C1—Tuned-tank capacitor.
C2—Coupling and biasing capacitor.
C3—RF filter capacitor.
L1—Primary winding of RF transformer.
L2—Secondary winding of RF transformer.
L3—Tickler or regeneration coil.
L4—Radio-frequency choke coil.
L5—Primary winding of AF transformer.
L6—Secondary winding of AF transformer.
V1—Detector-amplifier tube.
M1—Power supply.
M2—Headphones.

## Identification of Currents

In the absence of an RF signal, only two significant electron currents will flow in this circuit. These currents are:

1. Plate current through V1 (solid red).
2. Voltage-divider current through R2 (dotted red).

When an RF signal is being received, seven *additional* currents flow in the circuit. These currents are as follows:

3. RF input or signal current (dotted blue).
4. RF tank current (solid blue).
5. RF grid-driving current (also in solid blue).
6. Grid-leakage current (dotted green).
7. RF filter current through C3 (also in solid blue).
8. Audio current through headphones (solid green).
9. Feedback, or regenerative, current (also in dotted red).

## Details of Operation

In Fig. 5-1, when no RF signal is being received, only two electron currents—the voltage-divider and the tube current—are flowing. The voltage divider is placed across the power supply to provide the operator a means of controlling the amount of regeneration and, consequently, the amount of amplification available from the tube. The voltage-divider current (shown in dotted red) flows continuously from ground, from left to right through R2 and enters the positive terminal of the power supply, returning through the power supply to ground. Because of this continuous current movement through R2, a progressively higher positive voltage exists at each successive point from left to right. Thus, the position of the movable arm on R2 determines the amount of positive voltage applied to the plate of V1; this directly affects the amount of tube current that will flow.

The tube current (shown in solid red) consists of electrons which are drawn out of ground below the cathode. The heated cathode causes them to be emitted into the tube where they are attracted across the tube by the positive voltage on the plate. From the plate, they flow successively through L3, L4, L5, and R2. From R2 they are drawn into the positive terminal of the power supply, through which they must be delivered back to ground in order to have ready return access to the cathode of the tube.

Once stable conditions exist and when no signal is being received, this plate current is a pure DC. Consequently, no feedback or regeneration can exist between L3 and L2, or L5 and L6.

In Fig. 5-2 the additional currents which come into existence when a signal is being received from some transmitting station are shown. L1 may be considered as connected directly to an antenna; therefore the signal current induced in the antenna flows directly up and down through L1. This current is shown in dotted' blue; in Fig. 5-2, it is flowing upward through the coil. The continual up and down flow of this current through L1 induces a companion current to flow down and up through secondary winding L2. This current is shown in solid blue; in Fig. 5-2 it is flowing downward. This action delivers electrons to the lower plate of C1, making it negative, and withdraws electrons from the upper plate of C1, making it positive. Whenever the voltage on the upper plate of C1 is positive, it draws electrons toward it from any external circuit to which it may be connected. In this circuit it draws electrons upward through grid resistor R1 and onto the left-hand plate of C2. This current (shown in solid blue) becomes the electron current which drives the grid; in Fig. 5-2 it drives the grid to a positive peak of voltage.

(A simple rationale for correctly relating current directions to the resulting voltage polarities exists. Since electrons are themselves negative in nature, they will always flow away from a more negative area and toward a less negative area. Thus, an upward flow of these grid-driving electrons through R1 tells us that the voltage at the upper end of the resistor is more positive than that at the lower end.)

When the grid of V1 is made positive by this flow of grid-driving current, two important things happen within the tube: first, the amount of plate current flowing through the tube is increased; and second, grid leakage electrons flow out of the tube at the control grid.

The additional surge of plate current must flow upward through L3 on its way to the power supply. As this plate current increases, it induces a separate current in L2, to which coil L3 is inductively coupled. This new induced current, which is shown in dotted red, is the feedback current which provides the basic regenerative action which gives the circuit its name. Since it is flowing downward simultaneously with the downward flow of the tank current, the feedback current reinforces the tank current.

Fig. 5-3 shows the current conditions a half-cycle later. It is called a negative half-cycle because the grid-driving current is flowing downward through R1, making the voltage at the top of this resistor negative. This grid-driving current is itself being driven by the negative voltage on the upper plate of tank capacitor C1. This negative voltage results from the fact that the tank-current electron flow has reversed during this half-cycle, and

93

electrons are flowing upward through L2 to the upper plate of C1, making it negative.

The negative voltage at the control grid during this half-cycle restricts or reduces the plate current flowing through the tube. A *decrease* in the amount of current flowing upward through L3 can induce a decrease in the current flowing downward through L2, or it can induce an increase in a current flowing upward through L2. For convenience, the latter case has been depicted in Fig. 5-3. Since the feedback and tank currents are both flowing upward simultaneously, one reinforces the other, and regeneration of the received signal occurs on both half-cycles.

Because of regeneration, an extremely weak input signal flowing through L1 may be amplified many thousands of times. With the appropriate adjustment of R2 (which controls the amount of plate current through the tube), the circuit can be operated just below the point of oscillation. A slight increase in the coupling between L2 and L3, or in the plate voltage applied to the tube, would cause the circuit to go into self-sustained oscillations, even in the absence of an input signal. This adjustment is one of the major disadvantages of the regenerative detector.

On the positive half-cycles depicted by Fig. 5-2, grid-leakage current flows. The complete path of this current (shown in dotted green) begins as usual at the ground connection below the cathode of the tube. Whenever a control grid has positive voltage on it, it will attract some of the electrons from the electron stream passing through the tube. Once these electrons strike the control-grid wires, they cannot be re-emitted into the tube; therefore, they must exit via the control grid. Eventually, the grid-leakage electrons will flow downward through grid resistor R1 and back to ground. If R1 is made large enough (as it usually is in practical circuit design), the electrons cannot flow immediately to ground but will first accumulate on the right-hand plate of C2, thereby building up a negative voltage, known as a *grid-leak bias voltage*.

During the negative half-cycles represented by Fig. 5-3, the grid is negative; consequently, it does not attract any electrons from the plate-current stream crossing the tube. However, those electrons which had previously accumulated on the right-hand plate of C2 constitute the negative grid-bias voltage and will continue to discharge downward through R1. This action is made possible by the relationship between the large sizes of C2 and R1 and the time duration of an individual cycle of the signal current. The combination of C2 and R2 in this type of circuit will invariably form a long time-constant network.

C3 acts in conjunction with radio-frequency choke coil L4 as a filter whose purpose is to filter or remove the RF pulsations which characterize the plate-current stream. As each individual pulsation reaches the entrance to L4, it has a choice of flowing into the high impedance represented by the choke coil or the low impedance represented by the capacitor. Most of the strength of each pulsation will flow downward into C3 during the positive half-cycles of Fig. 5-2, driving an equal number of electrons downward from the lower plate of C3 into the ground connection. During the negative half-cycles depicted in Fig. 5-3, the plate current has diminished; therefore, the filter current through C3 reverses and flows upward.

The action of the radio-frequency choke, when confronted by RF pulsations in plate current, is interesting. The purpose of any such choke is, of course, to prevent or inhibit the passage of high-frequency current. As each pulsation of plate current enters this choke coil at its left hand terminal, the increase in current which it represents generates a small current flowing in the opposite direction. This current has been shown in blue, and, in

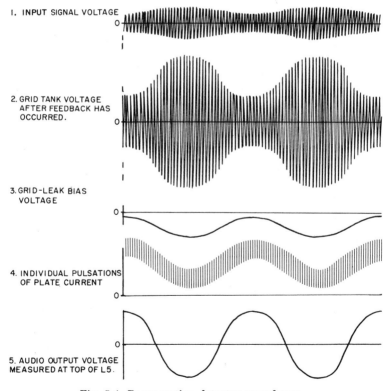

Fig. 5-4. Regenerative detector waveforms.

Fig. 5-2, it flows from right to left, thereby reducing the total change in current which would otherwise occur, and also satisfying the basic electrical property possessed by any inductance, namely, that it always reacts to any change in applied current flow in such a manner as to oppose that change.

In Fig. 5-3, when the negative grid-driving voltage causes a reduction in the amount of plate current through the tube and eventually through coil L4, the choke coil again reacts in such a manner as to oppose this reduction in current. Thus, it brings into existence the small choke-coil current (shown in solid blue), this time flowing in the same direction as the plate current, namely, from left to right.

The actions of C3 and L4 are essentially independent actions. The capacitor action is intended to filter as much of the high-frequency component (the pulsations) of the plate current as possible to ground before it reaches the load, which is the primary winding of audio transformer L5. The choke-coil action is provided to prevent these pulsations from reaching the audio transformer. Thus, when the two components are put together they provide a highly effective filter combination, with a low-impedance path in the desired flow direction (to ground in this example) and a high-impedance path in the undesired flow direction (the output load and the power supply).

Fig. 5-4 shows a graphical representation of certain current and voltage waveforms at various points in the regenerative detector circuit. Line 1 of Fig. 5-4 shows the very weak nature of the input signal as it is received in L1. Line 2 shows essentially the same waveform, after it has been vastly amplified or regenerated by amplifier tube action plus feedback action. Line 2 represents the strength or amount of tank current which flows in the tuned circuit (L2 and C1).

Line 3 (Fig. 5-4) indicates the relative strength of the grid-leak bias voltage which is detected by the grid-leak circuit combination of C2 and R1. Since any grid-leak bias voltage always consists of "trapped" or stored electrons, this voltage is always negative. We can see from a comparison of Line 3 with Line 2 that when a modulation peak occurs in the input signal, the individual RF cycles exhibit their maximum strength, and the leakage bias voltage reaches its maximum negative value. This is because the stronger RF cycles drive the grid to higher positive voltage values, and these higher positive voltages draw more grid leakage electrons out of the tube each cycle, and into storage on the right hand plate of C2.

Line 4 of Fig. 5-4 indicates the complex nature of the plate current flowing through V1. Since tube current is always a one-way current, or unidirectional in nature, the term pulsating DC is normally used to describe it. Inspection of Line 4 reveals that the plate current is pulsating at both a radio frequency and an audio frequency. Each cycle of the RF signal applied to the grid causes a small pulsation to occur in the plate-current stream. This action is accomplished primarily by the grid-driving current flowing up and down in R1. Each cycle of audio-modulating voltage which is de-modulated by the grid-leak bias arrangement causes a larger (and slower) pulsation to occur in the plate current.

Since L3 and L4 have extremely small amounts of inductance, the slow audio pulsations will pass through them without being affected. (The reactance of any inductor is directly proportional to the frequency of the current flowing through it.)

Lines 3 and 4 point out that when the maximum negative grid-leak bias voltage exists on capacitor C2, the audio pulsation in the plate current stream is at a minimum. We can arbitrarily decide to label this period as a negative half-cycle of audio. The plate cur-rent flows downward at all times through the primary winding of the audio transformer. When plate current is approaching its minimum value, the steady decrease in plate current will induce a current flow downward in winding L6. This is the current which is shown in solid green in Figs. 5-2 and 5-3.

When the plate current is approaching its maximum value, the steady increase in plate current will induce a current to flow up-ward in the secondary winding. Thus, a current which flows up and down at the basic modulation frequency through the head-phones is brought into existence.

## SUPERREGENERATIVE RECEIVER

It is only a short and logical step from the regenerative detector circuit of Figs. 5-1, 5-2, and 5-3 to the superregenerative receiver shown in Figs. 5-5, 5-6, and 5-7. There are two important differ-ences between the two circuits: (1) the regenerative detector portion of the superregenerative receiver is permitted to oscil-late at the frequency of the signal being received, and (2) a separate circuit, called a *quenching oscillator,* is provided to stop the oscillations.

### Identification of Components

The upper portion of Fig. 5-5 is a regenerative detector, similar in most respects (but not all) to the circuit explained previously. The components in Fig. 5-5 have been numbered wherever pos-sible to coincide with their counterparts in Fig. 5-1. The additional components which make up the quench oscillator are as follows:

R3—Grid-leak biasing resistor.
C5—Tuned-tank capacitor.
C6—Grid-leak storage capacitor.
C7—Coupling capacitor.
L7—Coupling inductor.
L8—Tuned-tank inductor (autotransformer).
V2—Quench-oscillator tube.

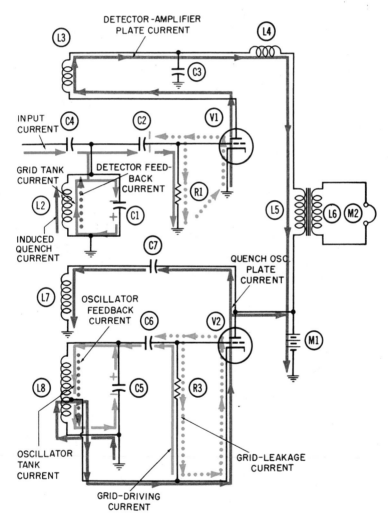

Fig. 5-5. Operation of the superregenerative receiver—negative
half-cycle of quench oscillator.

## Identification of Currents

The quenched-oscillator portion of this circuit operates at a much lower frequency than the signal frequency being received. A quench frequency of about 20 kc is normal. The quenching oscillator is a conventional Hartley oscillator. The various currents and the colors they are shown in are as follows:

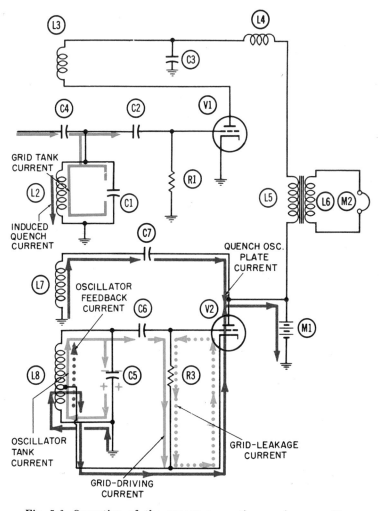

Fig. 5-6. Operation of the superregenerative receiver—positive half-cycle of quench oscillator.

1. Tank current (solid green).
2. Grid-driving current (also in solid green).
3. Grid-leak biasing current (dotted green).
4. Plate current (solid red).
5. Oscillator feedback current (dotted red).
6. Autotransformer feedback current (also dotted red).
7. Quenching current (solid red).

## Details of Operation

Figs. 5-5 and 5-6 are chosen to represent two alternate half-cycles in the operation of the quenching oscillator. It must be recognized that because of the much higher frequency of the received signal (to which the regenerative detector is tuned), many cycles of operation of the detector portion of the circuit will occur during a single cycle of the quench oscillator. The regenerative detector is normally operated just below the point of oscillation so that a slight increase in the amount of inductive coupling between L2 and L3 will provide sufficient regeneration and feedback to cause the detector circuit to oscillate.

This condition represents the maximum possible amount of gain, or amplification of the received signal. By itself, it is not an acceptable circuit technique, because once the oscillation is started it will continue even if the received signal goes off the air. Thus, the continued oscillation would indicate a signal which is actually not present. To protect against this eventuality, the quench oscillator turns the oscillating detector circuit off at its own basic frequency, namely, 20,000 times each second. Once the oscillating detector has been stopped from oscillating, it cannot be started up again unless the desired input signal is again on the air.

Fig. 5-5 depicts a positive half-cycle of the quench oscillator, when V2 is delivering a maximum surge of plate current. The oscillating tank current (shown in solid green) has moved downward through L8, thus delivering the electrons to the lower plate of C5, charging it to a negative voltage and making the upper plate positive. Whenever the upper plate is positive, it will draw the electrons of the grid-driving current upward through R3, making the upper end of R3 and the control grid of V2 positive. This releases a large pulsation of plate current into the tube.

This plate current (shown in solid red) must first be drawn upward through the lower portion of L8. An increase of this plate current in the upward direction through the lower portion of L8 causes a separate feedback current to flow at an increasing rate in the downward direction through the entire winding. This feedback current (shown in dotted red) flows in phase with the tank current, reinforcing it and supporting the quench oscillation.

The pulsation of plate current through V2 initially flows into the right-hand plate of C7, driving an equal number of electrons out of the left-hand plate and downward through L7 to ground. Because L7 is inductively coupled to L2, an upward flow of electrons will be induced in L2 during this half-cycle—this current is shown in dotted red. The polarity of the resulting "back electromotive force" or back emf associated with this new current flow will be positive at the top of L2 and negative at the bottom. This positive polarity is also applied to the grid of V1, enabling it to conduct electrons from cathode to plate. Consequently, if a signal is being received through C4, oscillations will be set up in the tank circuit made up of L2 and C1.

Fig. 5-6 depicts a negative half-cycle in the operation of the quench oscillator circuit. The electrons which make up the tank current in the quench oscillator have oscillated upward through L8, thereby delivering a large negative voltage on the upper plate of capacitor C5, as indicated by the green minus signs. Whenever this voltage is negative, it will drive electrons away from it along any available path. In this case, the only such path is downward through grid-driving resistor R3. (Electrons do not actually flow *through* C6 nor through any other capacitor for that matter, but normal capacitor action is such that when the negative voltage on C5 drives electrons onto the left-hand plate of C6, an equal number must flow out of the right-hand plate and downward through R3.) This downward movement of electrons through R3 causes a negative voltage at the upper terminal of R3 and the grid of V2, causing an inevitable reduction in the plate current flowing through the tube.

Two important actions stem from this reduction in plate current. First, the feedback current flowing in L8, (shown in dotted red), reverses its direction of flow so that it again flows approximately in phase with the tank current, thereby replenishing or sustaining its oscillation. Second, the electron current which was previously driven *downward* through L7 will now be drawn upward through this coil, and onto the left-hand plate of C7. This upward flow of current through L7 induces a counter current in L2, which is shown (in solid red in Fig. 5-6) flowing downward through the inductor.

The back emf associated with this induced current in L2 is assumed to be negative at the top of L2 and positive at the bottom. A negative voltage at the top of L2 will cut off the electron flow through V1, and stop all of the current movements previously existing in the regenerative detector portion of the circuit.

The input carrier signal may still be in existence and flowing in and out through C4; however, when it lacks the support of V1 and

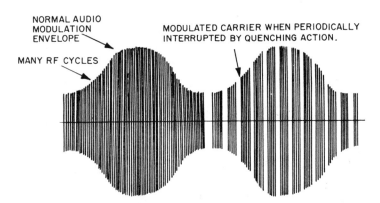

NORMAL AUDIO
MODULATION
ENVELOPE

MANY RF CYCLES

MODULATED CARRIER WHEN PERIODICALLY
INTERRUPTED BY QUENCHING ACTION.

Fig. 5-7. Modulated waveforms in quenching oscillator.

the feedback arrangement between coils L3 and L2, it cannot sustain an oscillation in the tank circuit made up of L2 and C1.

The quench circuit is provided against the specific contingency that the input carrier signal will periodically go off the air, and to stop, or quench, the oscillation going on in the RF tank circuit, L2 and C1, just in case this contingency may have occurred. If it has not occurred, no harm will have been done, because on the next succeeding positive half-cycle of the quench oscillator (such as is depicted in Fig. 5-5), the oscillation of electrons in the RF tank will be "reignited," so to speak. If, however, the input carrier signal has gone off the air, the oscillation in the RF tank cannot again be started up during the next succeeding positive half-cycle of the quench oscillator.

The ratio between the two oscillating frequencies will be perhaps 100 to 1, since the quench-oscillation frequency must be well above the range of the human ear—20 kilocycles is a fairly standard quench frequency—whereas the input carrier signal may well be 2,000 kc or higher.

In the event a continuous carrier signal, such as speech or music, is being received, one might wonder what effect the quenching action would have upon the results. Fig. 5-7 is a simplified waveform diagram around which an explanation may be built. The first half of this illustration shows one audio cycle of a typical modulated carrier signal, and may be considered similar in all respects to the modulated waveforms in Lines 1 and 2 of Fig. 5-4. The second half of Fig. 5-7 shows the modified waveform of the oscillation as it will actually exist in the radio-frequency tank circuit (L2 and C1) as a result of the quenching action.

The signal and quenching frequencies have a ratio of 100 to 1. The RF oscillator circuit centered around V1 will be turned on for perhaps 50 cycles during a single positive half-cycle of the quench oscillator. During a negative half-cycle of the quench oscillator, the RF oscillation will be quenched for perhaps another 50 cycles. If the audio frequency represented by the modulation envelope in the second part of Fig. 5-7 is 200 cps, 100 quenching operations will occur during a single audio cycle. These quenching operations will have no noticeable effect on the operation of the grid leak detector, or on the audio reaching the headphones, because of the time-constant relationship between C2 and R1.

When the values of C2 and R1 are multiplied together, the product is time in seconds. It is necessary only to choose the values of these two components so that their product in seconds will be long when compared to the time for one cycle of the quenching frequency (1/20,000th of a second), and short when compared to the time for one cycle of the highest audio frequency expected to be received (1/5,000th of a second). When the proper choice of components has been made, it can be said that the grid leak bias voltage stored on C2 cannot discharge fast enough to follow the rise and fall in the audio modulation envelope.

Thus, the grid voltage waveform shown in Line 3 of Fig. 5-4 will be reproduced even while the quenching process is occurring and will be an accurate reproduction of the original audio modulation sent out from the transmitter.

## REVIEW QUESTIONS

1. State the principal advantage and disadvantage of the regenerative detector circuit of this chapter.

2. What is the function of the voltage divider current which flows through R2 toward the power supply?

3. In the regenerative detector of Fig. 5-1, describe the effect on circuit operation if the available tap on R2 is moved farther to the right. Also, if it is moved farther to the left.

4. In the superregenerative receiver of Fig. 5-5, what are the two approximate frequency ranges for the two oscillations?

5. In this same circuit, what basic type of oscillator is used for the quench current?

6. Describe the particular circuit action which couples the quenching action of (V2) to the operation of the oscillating detector built around tube V1.

7. If a continuous audio-modulated carrier is being received by the superregenerative detector, why will the quenching action not be noticeable to the listener?

## Chapter 6

# TYPICAL SUPERHETERODYNE RECEIVER

In this chapter the final two stages in a typical superheterodyne receiver—the IF amplifier and the audio power amplifier—will be discussed. Then the methods for checking voltages and making signal-substitution tests for the entire receiver will be presented. Voltage checks and signal substitution tests are the two most common methods employed to isolate a trouble when servicing a receiver.

## IF AMPLIFIER

The function of the IF amplifier stage is to increase the strength of (amplify) the signal voltage which is supplied by the mixer to the control grid of the tube to the level required by the detector.

### Identification of Components

A typical IF amplifier circuit is depicted in Figs. 6-1 and 6-2. This circuit is composed of the following individual components, with functional titles as indicated:

R12—Cathode-biasing resistor.
C7—RF and IF filter or decoupling capacitor.
T1—IF input transformer (the secondary winding and the capacitor in parallel with it are part of this circuit).
T2—IF output transformer (the primary winding and the capacitor in parallel with it, are part of this circuit).
V2—Pentode tube used as IF amplifier.

## Identification of Currents

The following electron currents are at work in this amplifier circuit:

1. Grid-tank current (dotted blue).
2. Plate current (solid red).
3. Screen-grid current (dotted red).
4. Plate-tank current (solid blue).
5. IF filter current (dotted red).

## Details of Operation

The oscillation of electrons (shown in dotted blue) which occurs in the grid-tank circuit drives the control grid of V2 to alternate positive and negative values. It is supported, or replenished, each half-cycle by the movements of the tank current which flows up and down through the primary winding of T1. Fig. 6-1 shows the current in the primary winding flowing downward and the current in the secondary winding flowing upward. This action delivers electrons to the top of the tank, where they become concentrated on the upper plate of the tank capacitor, constituting a negative voltage at this point. Consequently, this half-cycle has been labeled as a negative half-cycle of operation.

Fig. 6-2 shows the current in the primary winding moving upward and the tank current moving downward through secondary winding of T1. This action delivers electrons to the lower plate of the tank capacitor, creating a deficiency of electrons on the upper plate. This deficiency constitutes a positive voltage; therefore Fig. 6-2 has been labeled as a positive half-cycle of operation.

*Plate Current*—During negative half-cycles (Fig. 6-1), the control grid of V2 will have its most negative voltage, and the plate current electron stream will be reduced to its minimum value. During the positive half-cycles (Fig. 6-2), the plate current stream is increased to its maximum value. Thus, the plate current is a form of pulsating DC, which flows continuously from cathode to plate within the tube, then downward through the primary winding of T2 to the power supply.

The pulsations in this plate current coming out of the tube support a new oscillation of electrons in the plate-tank circuit. This electron current is shown in solid blue. In Fig. 6-2 when another pulsation of electrons arrives from the tube, it reaches the upper plate of the tank capacitor simultaneously with the tank current which has moved upward through the primary winding

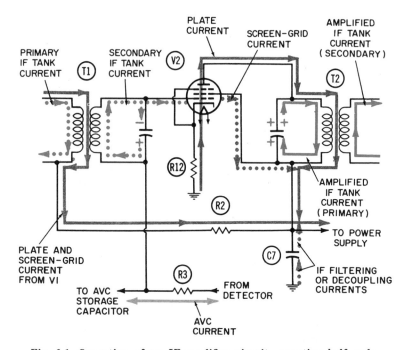

Fig. 6-1. Operation of an IF-amplifier circuit—negative half-cycle.

of T2, thereby reinforcing this tank current. The plate-tank current is an amplified version of the signal current which flows in the grid-tank circuit. This means that it is a stronger oscillation, or in other words that a larger quantity of electrons is oscillating in the plate tank than in the grid tank.

Another current (also shown in solid blue) is shown flowing in the secondary winding of T2 in Fig. 6-2. It is sustained by the primary tank current which oscillates up and down through the primary winding. As the primary current moves upward (Fig. 6-2), the secondary current moves downward; as the primary current moves downward (Fig. 6-1), the secondary current moves upward.

*Screen-Grid Currents*—The screen-grid current, and its associated filter current (both shown in dotted red) are the final set of electron currents in this circuit. The screen-grid current consists of electrons which are captured from the plate current stream within the vacuum tube. The screen grid has a fairly high positive voltage on it so that some of the negative electrons of the plate-current stream adhere to the wires of the screen grid. These electrons exit from the tube and rejoin the plate current below T2 and continue on to the power supply.

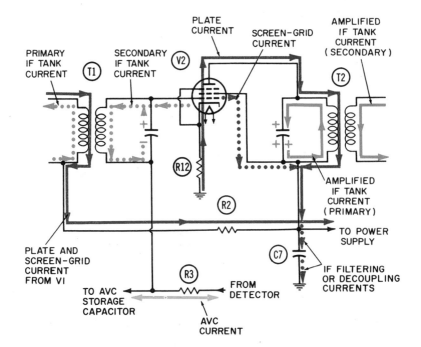

Fig. 6-2. Operation of an IF-amplifier circuit—positive half-cycle.

Like the plate current, the screen-grid current is also a pulsating DC. The pulsations occur during the positive half-cycles shown in Fig. 6-2. In Fig. 6-1 when the control grid is negative, the electron stream within the tube is reduced to its minimum value, and the plate and screen-grid currents are also reduced.

C7 filters out the fluctuations, or pulsations, in the plate and screen-grid currents. Fig. 6-2 shows such a filter action occurring. When a pulsation occurs in the screen-grid current, electrons flow onto the upper plate of C7, and other electrons are driven away from the lower plate to ground.

In Fig. 6-1, when no such pulsation occurs, electrons flow off the upper plate of C7 and into the power supply. This permits other electrons to be withdrawn from ground, and flow onto the lower plate of C7. The action of filtering out the pulsations in tube currents before they reach the power supply is frequently referred to as *decoupling* of the power supply.

*AVC Voltage*—The bottom of the grid-tank circuit is connected directly to the AVC storage capacitor (explained in Chapter 2). Since this capacitor has a permanent negative voltage stored on it, this voltage is also applied to the grid of V2 and acts as a permanent biasing voltage on that tube. Thus, as the AVC voltage varies, the gain of V2 is changed. The variations in grid voltage caused by the oscillation of electrons in the grid tank of this tube will alternately add to or subtract from this permanent biasing voltage.

## AUDIO POWER AMPLIFIER

The basic function of an audio power amplifier is to increase the strength of the audio signal delivered to it by the preceding amplifier, and to generate a heavy electron current at these same audio frequencies in order to operate the speaker.

### Identification of Components

A typical audio power-amplifier circuit is illustrated in Figs. 6-3 and 6-4. This circuit is composed of the following individual components, with the functions indicated:

R8—Grid-driving resistor.
R9—Cathode-biasing resistor.
R10—B+ dropping resistor (actually part of the power-supply filter system).
C12—Coupling and blocking capacitor.
C13—IF filter capacitor.
T3—Audio output transformer.
V4—Pentode power-amplifier tube.
SP1—Speaker.

### Identification of Currents

The following electron currents are at work in this power-amplifier circuit:

1. Grid-driving current (dotted green).
2. Plate current (solid red).
3. Screen-grid current (dotted red).
4. Speaker current (solid blue).
5. Plate and screen-grid currents from other tubes (also in solid red).

### Details of Operation

The grid-driving current (shown in dotted green) moves up and down through R8 at the audio frequencies being amplified. This current is in turn driven by the pulsations in plate current from the previous tube. Fig. 6-3 shows one such pulsation occurring, with plate current (shown in solid red) flowing onto the left-hand plate of C12. This action drives an equal number of electrons away from the right-hand plate of C12 and downward through grid resistor R8.

The grid-driving current flowing through R8 causes the voltage at the top of R8 to be negative. For this reason, Fig. 6-3 has been labeled as a negative half-cycle of operation. In Fig. 6-4, when the plate current pulsation is flowing out of the left-hand plate of C12, it draws the grid-driving current upward through R8. This indicates that the top of the resistor is more positive than the bottom.

In Fig. 6-3 when the top of R8 has its most negative voltage value, the plate-current electron stream flowing through V4 will be reduced to its minimum value. In Fig. 6-4 when the grid is positive, maximum plate current will flow.

*Power Amplification*—The construction of a power amplifier tube differs somewhat from that of a voltage-amplifier tube. A power-amplifier tube is constructed so that it will conduct a much heavier plate current at full conduction than a voltage-amplifier tube delivers. Electrical power varies as to the *square* of the current; therefore an amplifier tube which is capable of delivering wide extremes of electron current has been given the name of power amplifier. This title can be misleading because *all* amplifier tubes deliver their plate currents into some kind of a load, and consequently, some power is developed in each of these loads by these currents. A tube is called a power amplifier when it delivers a heavy enough current into its load to develop an appreciable amount of power.

The basic formula for computing power across a resistive load is:

$$P = I^2R$$

where,

P is the power developed in watts,
I is the current flowing through the resistor in amperes,
R is the resistance of the load in ohms.

The formula for computing power developed across an inductive load, such as the primary winding of T3, is:

$$P = I^2X$$

where,

P is the power in watts,
I is the current through the inductor in amperes,
X is the inductive reactance of the transformer primary in ohms.

*Plate Current*—The plate-current path starts at ground below R9. The electrons which make up this current flow upward

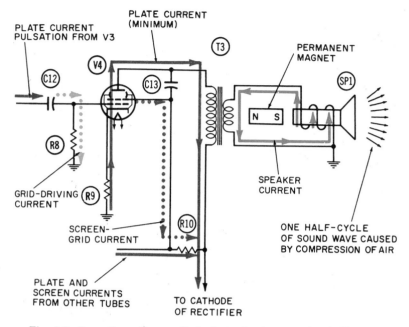

**PLATE CURRENT PULSATION FROM V3**

**PLATE CURRENT (MINIMUM)**

C12

V4

C13

T3

PERMANENT MAGNET

SP1

N   S

R8

GRID-DRIVING CURRENT

R9

SPEAKER CURRENT

SCREEN-GRID CURRENT

R10

ONE HALF-CYCLE OF SOUND WAVE CAUSED BY COMPRESSION OF AIR

PLATE AND SCREEN CURRENTS FROM OTHER TUBES

TO CATHODE OF RECTIFIER

Fig. 6-3. Operation of an audio-output circuit—negative half-cycle.

through R9, through the vacuum tube from cathode to plate, downward through the primary winding of T3, from where it flows directly to the cathode of the rectifier tube. All of the other plate and screen-grid currents join with this plate current at the right-hand end of R10, to be drawn eventually through the rectifier tube and delivered back to ground.

*Output Transformer*—Transformer action can be a very difficult physical action to visualize. Stated in the simplest terms, when a current, such as the plate current of V4, can be made to pulsate through one winding of the transformer, it will cause another current to flow back and forth in the other winding. The pulsations of plate current flowing downward through the primary winding of T3 cause the speaker current (shown in solid blue) to flow in the secondary winding.

When this plate current is increasing, as it does during the positive half-cycle of Fig. 6-4, the speaker current increases in the upward direction through the secondary winding. When the plate current decreases during the negative half-cycles (Fig. 6-3), the speaker current increases in the downward direction through the secondary winding. Since the plate current consists of continuous pulsations at the various audio frequencies, the speaker current will flow up and down through the secondary winding

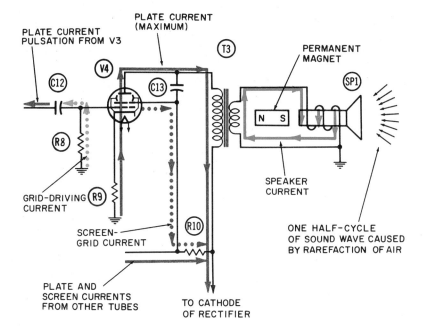

Fig. 6-4. Operation of an audio-output circuit—positive half-cycle.

(and through the moving coil of the speaker) at these same audio frequencies.

Like all similar output transformers, T3 has more turns in its primary winding than its secondary winding. This means that it is a current step-up transformer. (A current step-up transformer is the same thing as a voltage step-down transformer.)

The determination as to whether a transformer will step the current up or down is governed by a simple formula, which states:

$$\frac{I_p N_s}{I_s N_p}$$

where,

I_p is the current flowing through the primary winding,
I_s is the current flowing through the secondary winding,
N_s is the number of turns of wire in the secondary winding,
N_p is the number of turns of wire in the primary winding.

*Speaker Action*—The speaker is a typical moving-coil arrangement, which involves the use of two magnets—a permanent magnet and a temporary magnet (formed by the speaker voice-coil winding). The permanent magnet has been shown with its south pole adjacent to the left-hand end of the temporary magnet.

111

During the negative half-cycles shown in Fig. 6-3, the speaker current flows through the speaker voice coil in such a direction as to make the left end of the temporary magnet have a *south* magnetic pole. This causes it to be repelled by the adjacent south pole of the permanent magnet, and it moves to the right. Since the speaker cone is connected to the voice coil, it also moves. The movement of the speaker cone *compresses* the air in front of it and causes a half-cycle of a sound wave.

During the positive half-cycles depicted by Fig. 6-4, the speaker current flows in such a direction as to create a *north* magnetic pole at the left end of temporary magnet. This north magnetic pole will be attracted by the south magnetic pole of the permanent magnet, and its movement will cause a rarefaction of the air in front of the speaker diaphragm. This rarefaction of the air constitutes a second half-cycle of the sound wave.

*Lenz's Law*—The rule for relating the direction of electron flow around an iron core to the resulting magnetic polarity of that core is known as Lenz's law. If the iron core is grasped by the left hand so that the fingers point in the direction that the electron current is flowing through the coil, then the thumb points toward the temporary *north* magnetic pole of the electromagnet.

A moving-coil speaker is a current-operated device. The amount of movement of the iron core and the diaphragm to which it is attached depend on the amount of current flowing through the moving coil each half-cycle. The amount of diaphragm movement determines the loudness of the sound coming from your radio. Output transformers, such as T3, have more turns in their primary winding than in their secondary winding so that large fluctuations in plate current will be increased even more by the current step-up relationship between the windings.

## VOLTAGE CHECKING THE SUPERHET RADIO

When the superhet radio becomes inoperative, or "dead," there are a number of tests, progressing from very simple ones to more complex ones, which the technician can use to locate and remedy the source of trouble. Probably the first of these tests is a visual check to see if all the tubes are lighted. Some tubes may have metal envelopes, but in simple table model radios, most if not all tubes will have glass envelopes. When the radio is turned on, we can look inside the envelope (after approximately 18 seconds have elapsed) and see a red glow that indicates that the cathode is heating normally. In tubes with metal cases, we can usually tell whether the filament is heating by feeling the metal envelope to see if it is warm.

Fig. 6-5 shows the circuit diagram of a typical radio, with the filament heating current (in solid blue) flowing through its intended path. (Partial schematics of the various stages in this radio have been presented in the previous chapters.) The filaments for all five tubes are connected in series, so the same heating current must flow through every filament. If a single tube filament fails, no current can flow in any of them, so each must be checked on a tube tester. When the faulty tube is located in this manner, and replaced, the radio will usually operate again.

Once it is determined that the tubes are heating normally, the simplest method of isolating a faulty component is by the process known as voltage checking. This process requires only a single piece of test equipment—a standard voltmeter, along with a diagram showing voltages which can be expected at each tube electrode during normal operation. Each and every one of these electrode voltages has a value which is determined by one or more electron currents flowing through or along a certain resistive path. When each such current is understood and visualized, and when its complete path is recognized, the student or technician can infer a great deal about that current and about the components through which it flows by noting the voltage at the electrode where each current enters or exits from the tube.

The plate currents are superimposed on the circuit diagram in Fig. 6-5 in solid red. Each of these currents is drawn up from ground below the respective cathodes of the tubes, and across the tube by the high positive voltage at the plate. The point of highest positive DC voltage in the radio is the cathode of the half-wave rectifier tube V5; this positive voltage draws all of the plate currents through their respective plate-load circuits (primary of T1, primary of T2, R7, and primary of T3) to the filter circuit (R10, C14, and C15) and to the cathode of V5.

The DC voltages which exist at the principal electrodes of the vacuum tubes are all directly associated with the flow of these currents. A great deal of servicing information can be inferred by observing these DC voltages.

**Voltage Checking V1**

The schematic in Fig. 6-5 tells us that the cathode of V1 should be at ground voltage, the second control grid at $-12$ volts, and the screen grid and plate at $+105$ volts.

The negative or common ground terminal of the voltmeter should be applied to the chassis of the radio, and the positive probe should be touched in turn to each of the electrodes.

It could happen that L2 in the oscillator tank has burned out and opened so that the flow of plate current enroute from ground to the cathode is interrupted. When this happens, the actual voltage existing at the cathode will be slightly positive. Even though no plate current can flow if the ground connection is broken, some electrons will be drawn across the tube by the high positive plate voltage, creating an electron deficiency on the upper plates of C4 and C5. However, this small positive voltage cannot be measured unless an electrostatic voltmeter is employed.

When the normal test voltmeter is used, a much higher than normal positive voltage will be measured at the cathode terminal when L2 is open (it might be 75 to 100 volts in this instance). The reason for the high positive voltage is that the instant the meter probe touches the cathode terminal, the internal resistance of the meter completes the cathode circuit to ground. The meter resistance will be very high compared to the internal plate resistance of the tube. These two resistances form a voltage divider across the power supply. Therefore, even though the plate current is greatly reduced, a small current will flow through the meter and the tube. Because the meter resistance is the larger of the two resistances forming the voltage divider, most of the power supply voltage will be dropped across the meter resistance and read on the meter scale.

Note: Only an open-circuit in the lower half of L2 will cause this trouble. An open circuit in the upper half of L2 will not interrupt the flow of plate current, although it will surely stop the flow of oscillator tank current (shown in dotted green). This defect can be detected by signal substitution followed by a continuity check of the inductor.

If the measured cathode voltage proves to be zero, this does not necessarily prove that plate current is flowing, since the cathode voltage will also be zero when no plate current flows. The voltmeter probe should now be moved to the screen grid of V1, and then to the plate. Each of these electrodes should indicate approximately 105 volts, or only slightly less than the B+ voltage of 110 V. Both of these tube currents must flow through R2 enroute to the power supply, and the voltage drop across R2 accounts for the 5-volt difference between 105 and 110 volts.

If R2 has opened, these tube currents cannot flow; therefore, the voltage at the plate and the screen grid will be close to zero. An internal short in C7 would also result in this same symptom of zero voltage at the plate and screen grid. Heavy current would be flowing up from ground through C7, and to the right through R10 to the power supply.

The simplest check to determine which of these two components may have failed is to bridge R2 with another resistor of approximately equal value. If R2 has failed, this procedure will

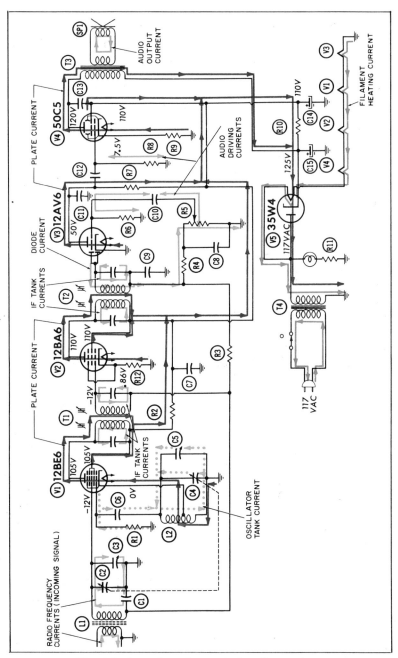

Fig. 6-5. Operation of a typical radio receiver.

provide an alternate path for the tube currents from V1, and the set may begin operating normally. If the capacitor has failed due to an internal short-circuit, one of its terminals must be unsoldered before the standard capacitor check can be made.

The AVC voltage can also be checked at this time, since it is the $-12$ volts existing at pin 7 of the tube. The AVC voltage is the accumulation of electrons which are stored on the left-hand plate of C1. These electrons are originally part of the detector current which flows through the diode portion of V3 and eventually finds its way through the AVC resistor R3 to C1. If C1 should become shorted, these electrons cannot accumulate but will flow or leak through C1 to the common ground connection between C1, C2, and C3.

A short circuit in either C2 or C3 would have the same effect of diverting all of the stored AVC electrons to ground, and of holding the second control grid of the tube at ground voltage. Each of these three capacitors should be given the standard checkout when this symptom occurs.

## Voltage Checking V2

The positive probe of the voltmeter can be applied in succession to the cathode, screen grid, and plate of V2. This gives valuable information about the components in the circuit. The positive cathode voltage of .86 volts exists solely because of the upward flow of plate current through R12. If the cathode voltage is significantly higher than this value, it probably means that the resistor has opened or increased in value. If R12 is open, a high positive voltage will be measured on the cathode as explained for V1. Also, the plate and screen voltages on V2 (and the other tubes) will increase by 5 to 10 volts. The reason for the increase of plate and screen voltages is that, with R12 open, V2 plate and screen current no longer flow through power supply filter resistor R10 and the voltage drop contributed by these currents no longer appears across this resistor. Temporarily bridging R12 with a low value resistor or even a straight wire should restore the set to operation and prove that R12 needs to be replaced.

Zero volts at the cathode indicates that R12 is probably all right, but tube currents are not flowing through it. A value between zero and $+.86$ volts at the cathode would mean that the tube currents are flowing in reduced quantity—an indication of reduced emission of the tube. This fact can be verified on a tube tester.

The plate and screen-grid voltages should also be measured. A value of 110 volts indicates that the tube currents are flowing normally. Any higher value indicates that these currents (or those of some other tube) are flowing in reduced amounts, or not at all. If the plate and screen-grid voltages are zero, this would mean that the line to the power supply is probably open.

If the screen-grid voltage is normal, and the plate voltage is zero, the primary winding of T2 could be open, so that screen current can flow, but plate current cannot.

The AVC voltage of −12 volts can be measured at the control grid of V2, just as it was measured at the second control grid of V1.

## Voltage Checking V3

The AVC voltage of −12 volts will exist at the two control grids previously mentioned, as well as at the two diode plates of V3. The mere existence of this voltage tells us that the tuned circuit associated with T2 is functioning normally and that the electron current through the diode portion of V3 is flowing.

A positive value of 50 volts should exist at the plate of V3. The difference between this value and the 110 volts of the B+ line (a 60-volt difference) is the voltage drop across the 470,000-ohm resistor, R7, caused by the flow of triode plate current through R7. If we find zero volts at the plate, the flow of plate current has probably been interrupted by R7 opening, or C11 may be shorted.

If the full value of 110 volts exists at the plate, we know that R7 is all right, but that no voltage drop exists across it because no plate current flows through it. This means that the tube is not conducting. Such a condition could be caused by a faulty tube, or the cathode connection to ground may have opened.

## Voltage Checking V4

If the electrode voltages on the three previous tubes have checked out satisfactorily, the cathode, screen grid, and plate of V4 should be checked. The desired cathode voltage should be +7.5 volts. This is the amount of voltage drop across R9 caused by the upward flow of plate current through it. If for any reason this current cannot flow, the cathode voltage will be at ground voltage, *as long as the current path through R9 has not been interrupted.* If R9 has opened, however, the cathode will be at a high positive voltage.

The plate should be at 120 volts, since it is connected directly to the point of highest voltage in the radio, namely, the cathode of rectifier tube V5. The plate current must flow through only the low resistance of the primary winding of T3. If the V4 plate voltage is zero, it most likely means that the primary winding of T3 is open.

If the plate voltage of V4 is equal to the full power-supply voltage of 125 volts, it means there is no voltage drop across the primary winding of T3 because no plate current is flowing through V4.

Zero voltage at the screen grid could mean that either C14 or C7 has shorted to ground. Either of these two defects would also have placed zero voltages at the plates and screen grids of V1, V2, and V3, and should have been detected in the earlier tests.

## SIGNAL SUBSTITUTION

After the electrode voltages have been checked and found satisfactory, a somewhat more complicated procedure known as signal substitution becomes necessary, in order to locate which component or components may have failed. To perform this series of tests, a standard signal generator is required. The signal generator must be able to provide:

1. An unmodulated RF signal at the highest local oscillator frequency to be encountered—approximately 2,000 kc.
2. A modulated carrier signal which can be varied from the IF to the top of the broadcast band—455 kc to 1,600 kc.
3. A 400-cps audio note.

The principle of signal substitution is to apply an artificially generated signal of the type normally encountered at each of several significant points within the receiver and to observe the operation of a limited portion of the receiver under these controlled conditions. The significant points in this case are principally the control grids and the plate circuits of each of the amplifier tubes. The normal signal one expects to find at each of these points is as follows:

1. Antenna input coil (L1)—a very weak modulated RF signal.
2. Second control grid of V1—same very weak modulated RF carrier signal.
3. First control grid of V1—a weak oscillatory signal whose frequency must always be 455-kc higher than the incoming carrier signal.
4. Plate circuit of V1—a weak RF signal at intermediate frequency of 455 kc.
5. Control grid of V2—a weak but amplified version of the IF signal at the plate circuit of V1.
6. Plate circuit of V2—an amplified version of the IF signal found in the grid circuit of V2.

7. Diode detector tank circuit—an IF signal of approximately equal strength to that in 6.
8. Junction of R4 and R5—a weak audio voltage.
9. Control grid of triode portion of V3—the same weak audio signal.
10. Plate of V3—an amplified version of this same audio signal.
11. Grid circuit of V4—same audio signal as in 10.
12. Plate circuit of V4—amplified version of same audio signal.
13. Speaker coil—same audio signal.

As with all other measurement devices, the signal generator method requires some kind of an output indicator. The speaker of the receiver serves this purpose very well. The procedure for checking out a receiver by the signal substitution method is to start at the bottom of the foregoing list and apply the appropriate signal to each point. If that portion of the circuit is functioning properly and if all prior portions of the circuit have been previously checked out (working backwards from the bottom of the list, of course), then a 400-cycle note should be heard from the speaker.

The reason the first check is made at the speaker is to be certain that our so-called "output indicator" is functioning properly. You must work backwards in an orderly fashion from plate to grid because when the faulty circuit is reached, there can be no question as to which circuit is at fault. We can only be sure of this if we know that all intervening circuits from the point in question to the output circuit (speaker) are functioning properly.

With the common ground of the signal generator connected to the common ground of the radio, the output probe of the generator should be touched to the top of T3. In order for the speaker to function properly, a closed circuit must exist through the secondary winding and through the speaker winding. The audio current (shown in green) must flow back and forth through this path. The 400-cycle setting of the signal generator provides this current, but a closed path through these two windings must exist in order for a 400-cycle note to be heard from the speaker.

Once the operability of the speaker has been established, the signal generator probe should be moved to the plate of V4. In normal operation, the plate current for this tube, shown in red, will pulsate at some audio frequency through the tube and downward through the primary winding of T3. The signal generator probe provides these pulsations for us, and if transformer T3 is functioning properly, an audio current will be induced in the secondary winding, and operate the speaker. If no signal is heard, then either the plate circuit is grounded, or T3 is not functioning. A grounded plate circuit would have been discovered on the prior voltage check.

If the signal is heard on this test, the signal-generator output should be turned down slightly, to allow for the gain which V4 should provide, and the probe should be applied to the control grid of V4. The probe will provide the grid driving current which has been shown in solid green in Fig. 6-5. This current moves up and down through R8, and develops the alternating positive and negative voltages which "drive" the control grid. If the tube and its associated circuitry are working properly, another 400-cycle note should be heard from the speaker.

With the generator still providing the 400-cycle note, the probe should be applied in succession to the plate and then the control grid of the triode portion of V3. Whenever the probe is moved to include an additional amplifying device such as a tube, care should be taken to reduce the output level of the generator to keep the speaker volume at a reasonable level.

The normal signal expected at the diode plates of V3 is an IF voltage which carries some audio modulation. Therefore, the signal generator should be reset to provide this kind of output, and the probe can be touched to either of the diode plates. The signal generator will then stimulate the appropriate IF tank current (shown in solid green in Fig. 6-5) in the tank circuit. Each positive half-cycle will cause one shot or pulsation of electrons to flow from the cathode to the diode plates of V3.

If resistors R4 and R5 and capacitors C8 and C9 are functioning, the tuned-tank circuit is all right and the detector portion of V3 is conducting normally, the diode current will flow as shown in solid green. Finally, if C10 and R6 are functioning, an audio frequency current will be driven back and forth through C10, and up and down through R6. Since we have already checked out all following circuits, this audio current flow through R6 should "drive" the amplifier portion of V3 and cause the 400-cycle note to be heard in the speaker.

When the workability of this much of the circuit has been established, the generator probe should be moved to the earlier check points in reverse order to that appearing in the list of check points. The next three check points all require the same type of signal during normal operation, namely, the IF signal modulated with 400-cycle audio. Since our generator is already set to provide this output, the probe should be applied in turn to the plate and control grid of V2, and then the plate of V1. The purpose in each case is to supply the normal signal current, which is shown in solid green in the four IF tank circuits of Fig. 6-5.

After these points have been checked, the signal generator should be reset to provide a substitute signal for the local oscillator. A value of 455 kc should be added to the frequency indicated on the tuning dial of the radio to determine the generator setting. For instance, if the receiver is turned to a *known* station which radiates on a frequency of 1,000 kc, the generator should be set to provide an *unmodulated* signal at 1,455 kc. By rocking the tuning dial slowly back and forth, it may be possible to "bring in" the desired station.

If none of the preceding tests has helped locate a faulty circuit component, a modulated RF signal from the generator should be applied to the top of the antenna coil (primary winding L1). This winding may have opened, either at the ground connection or at the point where it connects to the antenna. An open circuit at either spot would effectively prevent the necessary flow of the antenna current through this winding, and can account for an inoperative receiver.

### REVIEW QUESTIONS

1. In the IF amplifier circuits of Figs. 6-1 and 6-2, does the plate current of tube V2 flow intermittently or continuously? Is it a pulsating direct current, a pure direct current, or an alternating current?

2. In these same figures, four separate oscillating currents are shown in blue in four separate tank circuits. At what frequencies are these oscillations occurring?

3. The plate and screen grid currents must flow through R12 to reach tube V2, developing a *voltage* across R12. What is the polarity of this voltage and what functional name is usually assigned to it?

4. In what fundamental respect would the plate current of the power amplifier tube V4 in Figs. 6-3 and 6-4 differ from the plate current of an audio voltage amplifier operating at the same frequency?

5. Is audio output transformer T3 a voltage step-up or step-down transformer?

## Chapter 7

# TYPICAL TRANSISTOR RECEIVER

In this chapter a typical transistor broadcast receiver will be analyzed. First, the operation of the receiver and each electron current flow will be explained. Then the methods of checking the various voltages will be outlined. Finally, signal substitution tests will be given.

## TRANSISTOR BROADCAST RECEIVER

Figs. 7-1, 7-2, and 7-3 show three identical circuit diagrams of a typical transistor broadcast receiver. All of the electron currents which flow in this receiver during normal operation have been shown and identified in Fig. 7-1. In Figs. 7-2 and 7-3 these currents have been separated so that their actions may be more easily analyzed.

This receiver utilizes the superheterodyne circuit. Two stages of IF amplication are employed followed by a solid-state diode detector. The audio signal developed at the detector is then amplified by two voltage-amplifier stages, and push-pull power-amplifier stage. An adidtional stage is provided for overload protection.

### Identification of Components

The individual components which make up this radio and their functions are as follows:

R1—Volume control.
R2, R3—Base-biasing resistors for X1.

R4—Emitter-biasing resistor for X1.
R5—Oscillator-tank damping resistor.
R6—Emitter-biasing resistor for X3.
R7, R8—Base-biasing resistors for X2.
R9—Emitter-biasing resistor for X2.
R10—Base-biasing resistor for X3.
R11—Collector resistor for X3.
R12, R13—Base-biasing resistors for X4.
R14—Emitter-biasing resistor for X4.
R15, R16,—Base-biasing resistors for X5.
R17—Collector-load resistor for X5 and base-biasing resistor
    for X6.
R18—Emitter-biasing resistor for X6.
R19—Power-supply decoupling resistor.
R20—Emitter-biasing resistor for X7 and X8.
R21—Base-biasing resistor for X7.
R22—Base-biasing resistor for X8.
C1—AVC capacitor.
C2A—Emitter bypass capacitor for X6.
C2B—Power-supply decoupling capacitor.
C3—Input coupling and blocking capacitor.
C4—Oscillator-tank coupling capacitor.
C5—Bypass capacitor for R6.
C6—Feedback and neutralizing capacitor for X2.
C7—Emitter bypass capacitor for X2.
C8—Bypass capacitor for R10.
C9—Bypass capacitor for R12.
C10—Feedback and neutralizing capacitor for X4.
C12—IF filter capacitor.
C13—Audio coupling and blocking capacitor.
C14—Parasitic suppression capacitor.
C15, C16—RF tank capacitors.
C17, C18—Oscillator tank capacitors.
L1—Antenna-coupling transformer.
L2—Oscillator-tank transformer.
L3—First IF transformer.
L4—Second IF transformer.
L5—Third IF transformer.
T1—Audio interstage transformer.
SP1—Speaker.
X1—2N412 Converter transistor.
X2, X4—2N410 IF amplifier transistors.
X3—3458 Overload transistor.
X5, X6—2N406 Audio-amplifier transistors.
X7, X8—2N408 Audio output transistors.

M1—Battery power supply.
M2—Diode detector.

Note that all of the foregoing transistors are PNP type. It is standard practice to use one type of transistor—either PNP or NPN—in small systems, such as this one. This practice provides simplification in biasing and power-supply requirements.

## Identification of Currents

There are approximately 50 different electron currents at work in this radio during normal operation. These currents may be subdivided into seven main types, as follows:

1. Base-emitter current within each transistor—there is one such current for each transistor, making eight altogether (solid green).
2. Collector-emitter current within each transistor—there is one such current for each transistor, making eight in all (solid red).
3. Voltage-divider currents—there are six voltage-divider currents (solid blue). All of them originate at a ground connection and are drawn through certain resistors to the positive terminal of the power supply. These resistor networks, and the important function provided by the current through each one, are:

    *First Voltage-Divider Current (R2, R3, and R19)*—Provides a small positive base-biasing voltage for X1 at junction of R2 and R3, and a more positive emitter-biasing voltage at junction of R3, R4, and R19.

    *Second Voltage-Divider Current (R7, R8, R1, and R19)*—Provides a small positive base-biasing voltage for X2 at junction of R7 and R8, and a more positive voltage at junction of R8 and R1 for the biasing cathode of M2.

    *Third Voltage-Divider Current (R12, R13, and R19)*—Provides a small positive base-biasing voltage for X4 at junction of R12 and R13.

    *Fourth Voltage-Divider Current (R15, R16, and R19)*—Provides small positive base-biasing voltage for X5 at junction of R15 and R16.

    *Fifth Voltage-Divider Current (SP1, R21, and R20)*—Provides a low positive base-biasing voltage for X7 at the junction of the two resistors.

    *Sixth Voltage-Divider Current (SP1, R22, and R20)*—Provides a low positive base-biasing voltage for X8 at the junction of the two resistors.

4. Driving current for each transistor—these currents have been shown in the same colors as the currents which excite them, (dotted blue for X1 and X5; dotted red for X2, X3, X4, X6, X7, and X8).
5. Oscillating currents in the five tank circuits (dotted blue in RF tank, dotted green in oscillator tank, and dotted red in the 5 IF tank circuits).
6. Diode detector current through M2 (dotted blue).
7. Filter currents—these currents have not been shown in the diagrams, but they flow through the following capacitors to ground: C5; C1 and C2B; C7, C9 and C11; C8, C12 and C2B; C2A, C14.

## Details of Operation

In any transistor, two different electron currents—the base-emitter current and the collector-emitter current—must flow during normal operation. In the PNP transistor, such as those employed exclusively in this particular receiver, both of these currents *exit* from the emitter terminal of the transistor. The base-emitter current, which is frequently referred to merely as *emitter current,* enters the base terminal and flows through the emitter portion of the transistor before leaving at the emitter terminal.

The collector-emitter current, which is commonly referred to as *collector current,* enters the transistor at the collector terminal and flows through the collector, base, and emitter, within the transistor (in that order) before leaving via the emitter terminal.

In NPN-type transistors, both of these flow directions are reversed. The currents have the same names and they flow along the same two paths, except that they flow in opposite directions than for a PNP transistor.

The most important physical characteristic of the transistor, the one which permits it to function as an amplifier, is that property which permits the base-emitter current to control the flow of collector-emitter current. A small amount of base-emitter current flowing will permit a large amount of collector-emitter current to flow, and a small change in the amount of base-emitter current will cause a large change in the amount of collector-emitter current flowing. These current changes will always have the same sign, or phase, meaning that an increase in the base-emitter current brings an increase in the collector-emitter current, and vice versa.

Because of the foregoing characteristics, transistors are considered to be *current-operated* devices. However, the amount of base-emitter current which flows at any instant is precisely de-

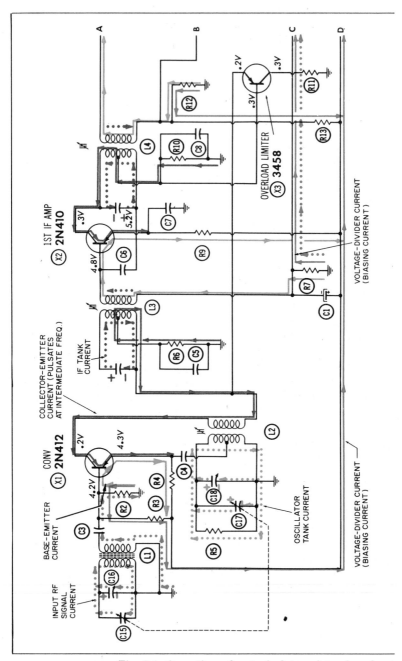

Fig. 7-1. Operation of a typical transistor broadcast

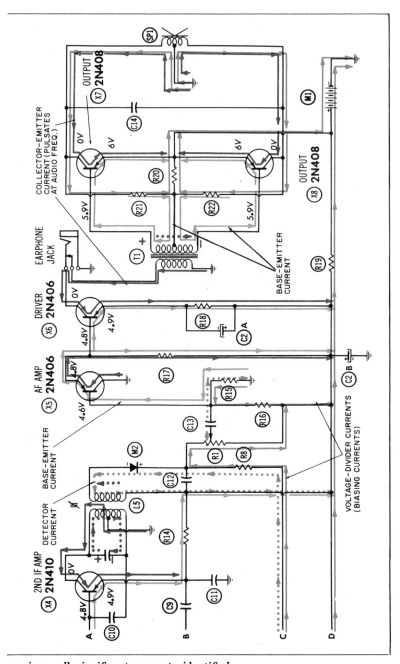

receiver—all significant currents identified.

termined by the voltage difference existing between the base and the emitter. In other words, these two terminals are "biased" by the voltages which exist on them. It is important, therefore, that the reader be able to understand how these voltages are achieved and see what factors cause them to vary, and in what manner and degree.

## OPERATION WHEN NO SIGNAL IS BEING RECEIVED

Consider the conditions which exist in the receiver when it is not tuned to a station. None of the signal currents (RF, IF, or audio) will be flowing, but all of the voltage-divider currents (solid blue) will be flowing. Fig. 7-2 shows these currents by themselves for additional clarity. Each of these currents will create an *initial voltage difference* of appropriate polarity to permit some electron current to flow from base to emitter within the transistor.

### X1 Biasing

The voltage at the junction of R2 and R3 is positive as a result of the voltage-divider current flow, and the base of X1 is positive. However, the voltage at the lower end of R3 is even more positive, because it is closer to the power supply. The emitter of X1 is connected to this point through R4; therefore it is more positive than the base, so that base-emitter current will begin flowing through the transistor.

This base-emitter current (shown in solid green in Figs. 7-1 and 7-3) flows upward through R2, through the transistor in the direction indicated, then through R4 from right to left, where it joins the voltage-divider current and is drawn through R19 and into the positive terminal of the battery. From the positive terminal of the battery, the electrons flow through the battery, out the negative terminal, and back to ground.

Once a small amount of base-emitter current begins to flow, the collector-emitter current also begins to flow. This current (shown in solid red in Figs. 7-1 and 7-3) is drawn upward through R6, through the lower portion of the primary winding of L3, upward through the secondary winding of L2, downward through the collector, base, and emitter of the transistor, then through R4 where it also joins the voltage-divider current on its journey to and through the power supply.

Each of these two transistor currents will create a separate component of voltage drop across R4. Each voltage drop will tend to make the left end of R4 more positive than the right-hand terminal. Since the transistor base is connected through R3 to the left end of R4, these two components of positive voltage will partially neutralize or nullify the original biasing condition caused by voltage-divider current flowing downward through R3. The net result will be a reduction in the amount of base-emitter current, and an accompanying reduction in collector-emitter current, from those amounts which would otherwise flow if R4 were not in the circuit.

The base-emitter and the collector-emitter currents will quickly stabilize at values that will allow the base voltage to remain slightly more negative than the emitter voltage. (A tenth or two-tenths of a volt difference between these two terminals is typical.) When the voltages at the base and emitter of a transistor are of such magnitudes that base-emitter current flows through the transistor, it is said to be *forward-biased*. If these voltages are such that base-emitter current cannot flow, then the transistor is *reverse-biased*.

In addition to their usefulness in describing the *total* voltage difference between base and emitter, these terms are also used to describe individual components of this total voltage difference, or bias. When used in this sense, the voltage-divider current flowing downward through R3 is said to contribute a substantial component of forward bias to the transistor, and the two transistor currents flowing through R4 contribute, or *add*, some reverse bias which reduces the forward bias. In the absence of any received signal, each of the transistor currents will be a pure DC.

The base-emitter and collector-emitter currents can never cut off the transistor entirely because, with no electron current flowing through R4, the emitter voltage would immediately rise to the high positive value existing on the main power-supply line. This would create so much forward bias that the transistor currents would again begin flowing.

Similar stories about DC operating conditions can be told about transistors X2, X4, X5, X7, and X8. Each of these transistor circuits is initially biased in the forward direction by the flow of one of the voltage-divider currents previously discussed. This initial forward bias starts the flow of base-emitter current which in turn starts the flow of collector-emitter current. In each case, the flow of the two transistor currents through an adjacent resistor will alter, or modify, the initial biasing conditions by contributing some reverse bias. And in each case, the amounts of the two transistor currents will settle down or stabilize at values which will permit the total bias (voltage difference between base and emitter) to remain at about a tenth of a volt in the forward direction. In the PNP transistor, this means that the emitter must be more positive than the base.

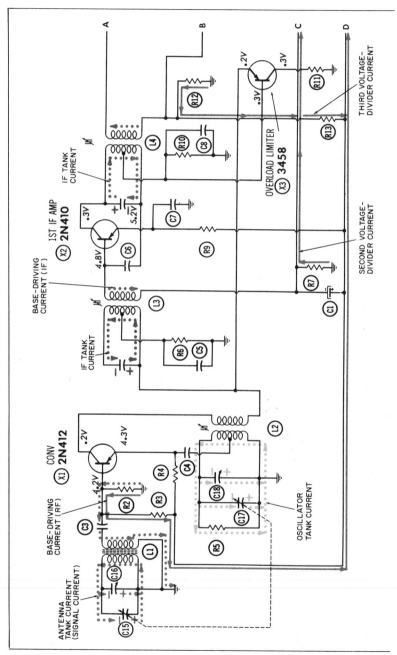

Fig. 7-2. Operation of a typical transistor broadcast

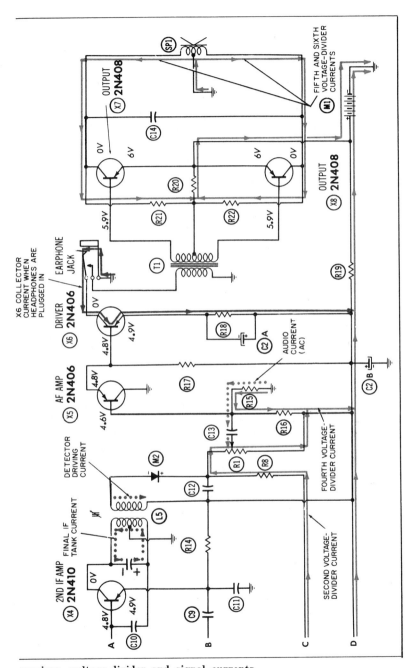

receiver—voltage-divider and signal currents.

## X6 Biasing

The manner in which this stage is biased differs from those discussed previously. Whereas the others are initially biased by one of the voltage-divider current actions, the base of X6 receives its operating bias directly from the emitter junction of the preceding stage. We have already seen how the two currents flowing through X5 must flow downward through emitter resistor R17, and in so doing how they reduce the voltage at the top of R17 from a high positive to a low positive value. This voltage becomes both the emitter voltage for X5 and the base voltage for X6. Since the emitter of X6 is connected to the high positive voltage, an initial base-emitter current, shown in solid green, will begin flowing through X6. This will cause the much larger collector-emitter current (solid red) to begin flowing. Both of these currents will flow downward through R18, and in so doing will reduce the positive voltage at the top of R18 from a high positive to a low positive value. These currents will stabilize or settle down at values which will keep the emitter of X6 only a fraction of a volt more positive than the base.

## Detector Current

The final electron current which flows in this transistor receiver when no station or signal is tuned in is the detector current (dotted blue in Fig. 7-1) through M2. The detector, of course, will conduct electrons in only one direction—from cathode (the straight line in the symbol for M2) to anode (the triangle in the symbol). This current originates at ground below R7 and flows successively through R7, R8, M2, the secondary winding of L5, and R19 before being drawn into the positive terminal of the battery. This current might very easily be classed as one of the voltage-divider currents, and at each point along its path is a slightly higher positive voltage than any point preceding it, and at a lower positive voltage than any point following it.

## OPERATION WHEN A SIGNAL IS BEING RECEIVED

The foregoing accounts for all of the electron currents which flow in the absence of a received signal. When the radio is tuned to a station, the five radio-frequency currents come into existence. The first one (shown in dotted blue in Figs. 7-1 and 7-2) flows in the RF tuned-tank circuit composed of C15, C16, and the primary of L1. Each half-cycle of it induces a companion current to flow in the secondary circuit, which includes the secondary winding of L1, C3, and R2. Current directions and voltage polarities have been chosen in Fig. 7-1 so that this secondary current flows *downward* through R2 during this particular half-cycle, developing a small component of negative voltage at the top of R2 which must be subtracted from the normal positive base voltage of 4.2 volts. In a PNP transistor, a less positive voltage at the base constitutes "forward bias" and drives an additional amount of base-emitter current through the transistor. This, in turn, causes an increase in the amount of collector-emitter current.

A completely separate oscillation of electrons will meanwhile be occurring at a higher frequency in the oscillator tank circuit. This tank circuit (L2, C17, C18, and R5) is designed so that the oscillator frequency will always be 455 kc higher than the carrier frequency. Part of the oscillatory voltage is coupled via C4 to the emitter of X1. An instantaneous voltage polarity for this tank oscillation has been chosen in Fig. 7-1 so that the emitter has been made temporarily more positive than its normal voltage of 4.3 volts. This also constitutes forward bias in the PNP transistor so that another additional component of base-emitter current is encouraged to flow, drawing another additional component of collector-emitter current through the transistor.

This additional component of collector current must first flow upward through the secondary winding of L2; in so doing, it induces a feedback current to flow downward in the primary winding. Since this feedback current is approximately in phase with the tank current, the oscillation will be sustained or replenished during each cycle of operation.

Since the biasing conditions are being simultaneously varied by two separate frequencies, the collector current will be caused to pulsate through the external circuit at each of these two frequencies. As in the case with vacuum tube mixing and converting circuits, the collector current also pulsates at other frequencies, such as the sum and difference of the two applied frequencies. The tank circuit at the primary of L3 is tuned to this difference frequency of 455 kc so that each pulsation which occurs in the collector current at this frequency will surge downward through the lower half of the inductor and sustain or reinforce one cycle of the oscillation.

The IF oscillating current in L3 and its associated capacitor is shown in dotted red. Current directions in Fig. 7-1 are chosen as downward in the primary winding, thereby inducing an upward current in the secondary. This secondary current delivers electrons to the base of X2, thereby increasing its forward bias during this half-cycle and causing a momentary increase in the flow of both base-emitter and collector-emitter current through the first IF amplifier transistor X2.

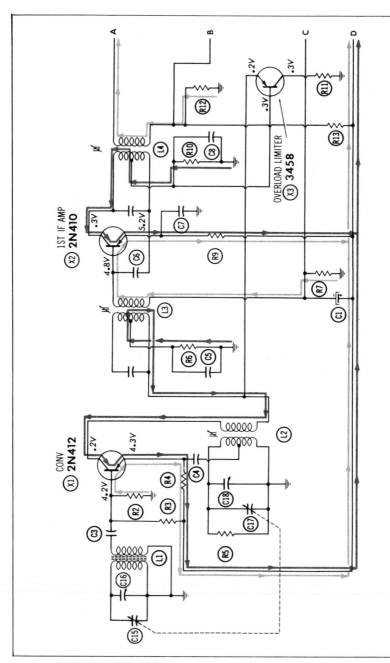

Fig. 7-3. Operation of a typical transistor broadcast

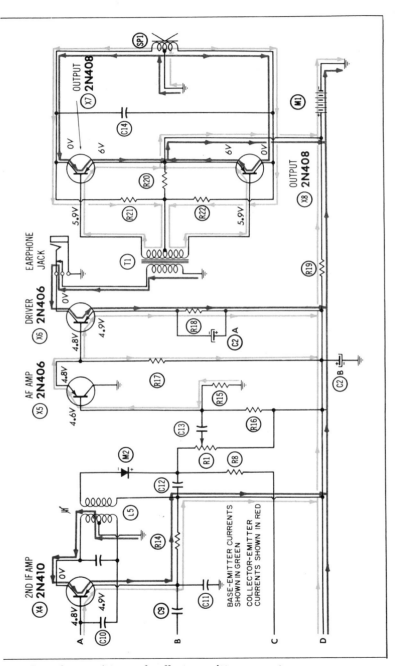

receiver—base-emitter and collector-emitter currents.

The collector-emitter current of X2 flows only through the upper half of the primary winding of L4. However, this provides sufficient coupling to the entire primary winding so that another IF tank current oscillation will be set up and sustained by means of autotransformer action. In Fig. 7-2 the upward pulsation of collector current through the primary winding is indicated as being in phase with the upward flow of tank current. In the secondary winding of L4, the induced current is shown as flowing downward, removing electrons from the area near the base of X3 and thus making the base more positive. This constitutes reverse bias, with the result that the amounts of base-emitter current and collector-emitter current through X4 will be reduced.

The final oscillation of electrons at the intermediate frequency occurs in tank circuit composed of L5 and its associated capacitor. Each cycle of it is sustained by a single pulsation of the X4 collector current as it surges through L5. The tank voltage polarity shown in Fig. 7-1 corresponds to the half-cycle when a pulsation of collector current is not occurring. This polarity is shown reversed in Fig. 7-2 along with all other tank voltage polarities and current directions.

The flow of tank current up and down through the primary winding of L5 induces a companion current to flow down and up respectively through the secondary winding. This secondary current and the induced voltage associated with it in effect drive diode M2 and cause it to detect or demodulate the audio intelligence which has been carried to the antenna by the RF carrier signal, and which has been carried through the "front end" of the radio by the converter and IF amplifiers.

### Detector Current

The detector current which flows through M2 is shown in dotted blue. This current flows continuously, originating at the ground connection below R7, flowing upward through R7 and R8, from cathode to anode of M2, downward through the secondary winding of L5 to the main power supply line of the receiver. When no signal is being received, this current flows as pure DC through the resistive portion of the path, and as pulsating DC through M2 and L5. This feature is made possible by the integrating action of C12 along with R8 and R7. A positive charge will be accumulated on the right hand plate of C12. Electrons will flow continuously into this point from R8, tending to discharge it to zero. But electrons are also drawn continually away from this point to flow through M2 and on to the positive voltage of the power supply.

When no signal is being received, a condition of equilibrium is established. The quantity of electrons flowing into C12 equals the quantity being drawn out, and a positive voltage exists on the right-hand plate. When a signal is being received, the voltage at the upper end of the secondary winding of L5 fluctuates between higher and lower positive values because of the movements of the IF current (shown in dotted red) induced in this winding. In Fig. 7-1, this IF current and associated voltage polarity are such that the upper electrode (the anode) is made less positive than it was before. This restricts the flow of electron current through M2.

In the alternate half-cycle shown in Fig. 7-2, the anode of M2 is made more positive by the IF current/voltage combination in the secondary winding of L5. This momentarily increases the flow of electrons through M2. Because of the large size of C12, the fluctuations in detector current are drawn directly from the right hand plate of C12 without causing a significant change in its total voltage.

When a modulated carrier signal is being received, the strength of the IF oscillation in the primary of L5 varies from cycle to cycle. A modulation peak is characterized by a succession of relatively strong individual cycles of IF. A modulation trough is characterized by a succession of relatively weak IF cycles. One cycle of audio voltage consists of one modulation peak and one modulation trough; together they will encompass many hundreds or even several thousand cycles of the IF oscillation.

The audio or modulating voltage, which is the intelligence we seek to hear from our radio, makes its first appearance in the radio on the right-hand plate of C12. The positive voltage at this point rises and falls at an audio rate. During modulation peaks, the strong IF cycles will draw an increased number of electrons away from C12, and the positive voltage at this point must increase. During modulation troughs, the weaker IF cycles will draw a reduced number of electrons away from C12, and the positive voltage at C12 will go up again. Thus, the positive voltage on C12 rises and falls in accordance with the strength and the frequency of the modulating voltage (the audio).

The second voltage-divider current flows downward through R1. When no modulated signal is being received, this current is a pure DC. When an audio voltage appears on C12, this voltage-divider current will pulsate at an audio rate. When the voltage on C12 reaches its most positive value during the modulation troughs, it approaches more nearly the value of the voltage existing at the bottom of R1. Thus, there will be a reduction in the amount of current flowing downward through the volume control during modulation troughs.

When the voltage on C12 reaches its least positive value during modulation peaks, it differs by a greater amount from the voltage which exists at the bottom of R1. Consequently, the amount of electron current flowing downward through R1 must increase during modulation peaks.

As a result of these pulsations in current flowing downward through R1, the voltage at any point along R1 will also pulsate at the same audio frequency. This pulsating voltage is coupled to C13, where it drives a small component of current up and down through R15. R15 functions as a base-driving resistor in much the same manner that a grid driving resistor functions in a vacuum tube circuit. During modulation peaks when the voltage divider current flowing downward through R1 increases, electrons will flow onto the left hand plate of C13, driving an equal number out of the right hand plate and downward through R15. This action develops a small component of negative voltage at the top of R15 which must be subtracted from the positive voltage developed at that point by the upward flow of the fourth voltage-divider current and the base-emitter current through this same resistor.

The reduction in positive voltage at the base of X5 constitutes forward bias in the PNP transistor, with the result that both the base-emitter and the collector-emitter currents through X5 will increase. This constitutes a half-cycle of the audio signal. The base driving current has been shown in dotted blue. It flows downward in Fig. 7-1.

Fig. 7-2 shows the base-driving current flowing upward through R15. This action constitutes the half of the audio cycle corresponding to a modulation trough. When it flows upward through R15, it adds an additional component of positive voltage to the other positive voltages already there. An increase in the positive voltage at the base of a PNP transistor constitutes reverse bias, so that both the base-emitter and collector-emitter currents will decrease during this half-cycle.

During the modulation peak, the increase in transistor currents through X5 will develop an increased voltage drop across R17, which can be observed as a decrease in the positive voltage existing at the emitter of X5, the base of X6, and the upper end of R17. Thus, an additional component of forward bias is applied to the base of X6 so that its two transistor currents also increase during a modulation peak.

## Push-Pull Output Amplifier

The two output transistors (X7 and X8) are connected in push-pull arrangement to provide a heavy audio current to drive speaker SP1. Operating, or bias, voltages for these transistors are selected so that when one of them conducts, the other one will be cut off.

Both transistors are driven from the secondary winding of T1. The collector current for X6 pulsates upward through the primary winding of T1 at the audio frequency, and each pulsation induces a half-cycle of current to flow downward in the secondary winding. The induced voltage associated with this induced current is indicated in Fig. 7-1 as positive at the top of the secondary winding and negative at the bottom. This applies reverse bias to the base of X7, making the base more positive than the emitter and cutting off the flow of both transistor currents through X7.

It also applies forward bias to the base of X8, making its voltage significantly less positive than the 6 volts applied to the emitter, and causing an increase in base-emitter current, and a consequent heavy surge of collector-emitter current through X8.

In the succeeding half-cycle an opposite set of conditions prevail. The collector current through X6 decreases, the voltage induced across the secondary winding of T1 is negative at the top and positive at the obttom. This cuts off both of the transistor currents through X8, and causes an increase in base-emitter current through X7, and a resultant heavy collector-emitter current through X7.

The collector currents for X7 and X8 originate at the center-tapped ground connection of speaker SP1. Each of these currents flow through only half of this winding, and of course they flow in opposite directions. Since they flow on alternate half-cycles and in opposite directions through this winding, the speaker diaphragm will be alternately driven to the right and left at the frequency of the audio modulating voltage carried by the original carrier signal.

The headphone jack above X6 in the diagrams can divert the collector current of X6 so that it will flow either through the phones or through the primary winding of T1, but not through both. Headphones require a much smaller power than a speaker; therefore the pulsations in the collector current of X6 will be adequate to operate the phones without the additional amplification provided by X7 and X8. The headphone current path has been indicated in Fig. 7-2. The headphone current is, of course, identical to the collector-emitter current of X6.

### Operation of the Overload Limiter

The overload limiter, X3, is reverse-biased during normal operation by making the base voltage (+0.3 volts) more positive than the emitter voltage (+0.2 volts) so that no base-emitter current can flow. The base voltage is developed by the upward flow of collector current for X2 as it passes through R10. (This same voltage also biases the collector of X2.)

The overload limiter is a form of noise limiter and might also be classed as an "instantaneous automatic volume control" which is capable of responding to a single strong noise pulse, or a very sudden increase in carrier signal strength. Consider the various circuit actions which accompany the arrival of an excessively strong cycle or noise pulse.

The oscillation of electrons which goes on in L4 is sustained once each cycle by a pulse of collector current being drawn through R6 and the primary of L3 on its way to the collector of X1. A strong pulse will set up an excessively strong cycle of oscillation in the tank, and this will be amplified by X2 so that an even larger oscillation will occur in its collector tank. A portion of this tank voltage is coupled to the base of X3; when the instantaneous tank voltage at the point where the primary winding of L4 is tapped is negative, the positive voltage at the base of X3 may be reduced to the point where it is *less* positive than the emitter voltage so that X3 begins conducting.

This conduction process in X3 will last for only a small fraction of a cycle, but the collector current of X3 must flow from the emitter to the bottom of L3. In doing so, it will deliver electrons to the L3 tank circuit. In order for the necessary limiting action to take place, this delivery of current must occur when the instantaneous voltage at the bottom of the tank has been made *positive* by the oscillation of electrons. When this condition is met, the strength of the oscillation in L3 will be reduced for that particular cycle. Thus, all subsequent derivations of this IF tank current will also be reduced in strength, and in this sense transistors X2 and X4 will be protected against "overloading" by too strong a signal.

Fig. 7-2 indicates the voltage polarities which must exist in the tank circuits in order for this form of degenerative feedback to occur. If one of these polarities should become reversed, then the electrons from the collector current of X3 would arrive at the bottom of L3 at the wrong time when the bottom of the tank is already negative as a result of the tank oscillation. The oscillation would be reinforced instead of reduced in strength.

### Automatic Volume Control

The AVC circuit of this radio is almost identical in its operation and construction to the positive AVC circuit discussed in Chapter 2. Therefore the circuit actions will not be discussed again here. C1 is the AVC storage capacitor, and R8 is the principal AVC filter resistor. This filter combination will react appropriately to reduce the signal strength when there is a long succession of strong carrier cycles. The overload limiter could theoretically perform this function by reducing the strength of each one of these cycles. However, this would be highly undesirable on a continuing basis, because when an individual cycle is reduced in strength in this manner, its original sinusoidal wave shape is highly distorted. The audio intelligence carried by the modulation envelope of a wave shape whose every cycle required an arbitrary and probably varying reduction in size would surely suffer from such an arrangement.

## VOLTAGE AND RESISTANCE CHECKS

The foregoing accounts for all of the electron currents which flow in the receiver in the absence of a received signal. Counting the 6 voltage-divider currents, the 14 transistor currents, and the detector current, it comes to 21 currents in all. In the two repair processes, known as voltage checking and resistance or continuity checking, these are the currents we are trying to look at. If any single one of these currents is significantly altered in quantity from its normal rate of flow, that fact can be discovered by the very simple maintenance process known as voltage checking. A significant variation of any one of these currents can occur in either direction. A current can be interrupted entirely, or it can be flowing in a much greater amount than is intended by the circuit design. Any such change in a particular current will inevitably be accompanied by a change in voltage at one or more points along the current path. When this current path is clearly understood, and when the current itself can be visualized, any change in an operating voltage can be instantly translated, or interpreted, in terms of a change in current flow of a particular current. Once this interpretation has been made, a closer look can be taken along the entire path of that current, and the faulty component can be quickly isolated.

Fig. 7-2 shows the operating voltage at each element of each transistor. For example, a base voltage of +4.2 volts, an emitter voltage of +4.3 volts, and a collector voltage of +.2 volts is shown for X1. How these voltages are achieved was discussed previously and will not be repeated here.

Suppose that the radio is inoperative, or dead, due to unknown causes. Where and how do we start to isolate the trouble? Voltage checking at various key points with a DC voltmeter set on an appropriate low scale is the simplest and most obvious approach. With the common ground probe of the voltmeter connected to the ground terminal, the positive probe of the voltmeter should be touched to the positive terminal of the battery M1. If the voltmeter indicates that M1 is delivering its full rated voltage of 6 volts, the positive probe should be moved to the left hand terminal of R19. Since all of the voltage divider currents, all of the transistor currents, and the detector currents flow through R19 from left to right, a voltage drop must be generated across R19 in accordance with Ohm's law. This voltage drop is subtracted from the 6-volt output voltage of M1 so the voltage at the left terminal of R19 will be slightly less than 6 volts.

If this voltage should read zero, it could mean one of two things, either R19 has burned out or is otherwise open, or that the main power-supply line has become grounded somewhere within the set. The quickest way to determine which one of these two conditions may exist is to momentarily place another resistor (of approximately equal value, but this is not important), across the terminals of R19. If the voltage at the left terminal of R19 then jumps up, it is a clear indication that R19 has opened, and should be replaced.

If the voltage at the left terminal of R19 remains at zero, the main power-supply line has become grounded somewhere. This could have happened within any filter capacitor which connects the line directly to ground. Inspection of the circuit diagram indicates that C2B is the only capacitor which meets this qualification. Disconnect one end of C2B from the circuit; if the voltage on the line jumps up, C2B is shorted and should be replaced.

Assume, however, that the voltmeter indicates the proper voltage at the left terminal of R19. This tells us that most of the divider and transistor currents are flowing normally. Further, voltmeter checking can indicate exactly which ones are and which ones are not flowing. The positive probe of the voltmeter should now be placed on the base of X1, where it is expected to indicate +4.2 volts. If the voltmeter reading is zero, the voltage-divider current is not flowing through R2 and R3. Since resistors are more apt to open than to become short-circuited, each one should be considered in turn for the possibility that it may have failed and become an open circuit.

If R3 has opened internally, the voltage-divider current cannot flow through it, and the transistor base will be connected directly to ground through R2. This could account for the very symptom we are confronted with—zero voltage instead of +4.2 volts at the base of X1. A visual inspection and perhaps a continuity check of R3 is now in order to determine its condition.

Suppose now that R2 has burned out and opened, this would not account for the symptom. Instead, we would find the full power-supply line value at the base, because the base is connected directly to the line through R3, and no current is flowing through R3 because it cannot get up through R2 in the first place. Since no current flows through R3, no voltage drop or difference can exist between its terminals. Consequently, an indication of full power-supply voltage at the base of X1 should lead us immediately to suspect R2 of having failed, and a visual and continuity check should be instituted. The continuity check may be preceded by the more simple test of bridging R2 temporarily with another resistor of approximately equal value. If the base voltage drops immediately to the desired value of +4.2 volts, it tells us that the voltage-divider current is now flowing normally through the alternate resistor and R3. No further test is needed to ascertain that R2 is not conducting electron current. In other words, it has failed and should be replaced.

There is one other possible cause for the base of transistor X1 being at zero voltage. C3, which couples the input carrier signal from the antenna tank circuit to the base of X1, may have become internally shorted, so that the base of X1 is connected directly to ground through the low resistance of the secondary winding of L1. To eliminate this as a possibility, the coupling connection from C3 to the base must be temporarily opened, probably by unsoldering one of the capacitor terminals. If this action results in a normal base voltage reading, we know that voltage divider current is now flowing normally through both R2 and R3. No further tests should be necessary to tell us that C3 has failed and should be replaced.

Suppose, however, that the meter reading indicates that the normal base voltage of +4.2 volts exists. The positive probe of the voltmeter should now be moved to the emitter terminal of X1, where we hope and expect to find +4.3 volts. If, instead, zero voltage is found, it can mean one of two things. Either R4, which connects the emitter to the positive line, has opened, or C4 has shorted so that the emitter is connected to ground through the low resistance primary winding of L2. A resistor of value equal to R4 may be bridged across its terminals. If this action results in a normal emitter reading of +4.3 volts, we know that the two transistor currents are now flowing normally through the alternate resistor and they were not flowing through R4. The usual visual and continuity check of R4 should be made; there can be little doubt of their outcome (assuming that good solder joints existed at its terminals).

To determine whether C4 is internally shorted it will be necessary to open the coupling connection from the oscillator tank by unsoldering one of the terminals of C4. If this action results in a normal meter reading for the emitter voltage, C4 is the faulty component and should be replaced.

If our initial emitter voltage reading has a positive value, greater than the desired value of +4.3 volts, a different group of failure possibilities are implied. If the emitter exhibits the full power-supply voltage, the most likely reason is that neither of the two transistor currents are flowing through R4. Therefore they cannot generate the expected voltage drop across it, and the resistor's two terminals must be at the same voltage. Outright failure of the transistor to operate may be the reason for this symptom; however, you should first ascertain that the collector portion of the circuit is functioning properly. R6 may have opened, and since the collector current for X1 must flow through R6 before it reaches the collector and R4, it might be the cause of the trouble. If this were the case, the base-emitter current could still be flowing through the transistor and R4. The base-emitter current may be only one-fiftieth or so as large as the collector current, consequently, when flowing by itself, the voltage drop across R4 would be so small it would be hard to detect.

The next step is to move the positive voltmeter probe to the collector terminal of X1, where the schematic tells us to expect voltage of about +0.2 volts. This positive voltage is generated at the upper terminal of R6 by the upward flow of collector-emitter current through it. A zero voltage reading at the collector would most likely indicate that an unintentional ground had occurred, perhaps within C5 or between the primary and secondary windings of L2 or L3. The capacitor should be checked first by unsoldering one of its terminals and noting if the collector voltage returns to normal. If it does not, the trouble lies elsewhere, and a more detailed continuity check with an ohmmeter should be made between the various terminals of L2 and also L3.

If R6 has opened, the voltmeter will probably indicate some indeterminate value of positive voltage, but higher than the normal 0.2 volts, at the collector. This would in fact be the positive voltage which was stored on the upper plate of C5 at the instant that R6 failed. This stored voltage may actually increase slightly after the resistor fails, as a few additional electrons are drawn out of the upper plate of C5, to pass through the transistor as a tiny component of collector-emitter current.

If failure of R6 is suspected, the usual simple expedient of bridging it with another resistor of equal value can be used to verify the fact. If transistor voltages return to normal, R6 should be replaced. If bridging R6 does not isolate the trouble, check the windings of L2 and L3 for possible open circuits.

## Voltage Checking Other Stages

A similar procedure and analysis may be followed to locate faulty components associated with any of the other stages in the receiver. The voltages at each terminal of each transistor are given in Figs. 7-1, 7-2, and 7-3. The positive voltmeter probe should be touched in turn to each of the terminals of the transistors, and any abnormal reading can then be interpreted in relation to the current or currents which bring this abnormal reading into existence. Once we recognize which of the currents has changed from its normal or expected value, only elementary deductive reasoning, is required to tell why this current change must have occurred. This leads us very quickly to the failed component.

## SIGNAL SUBSTITUTION TESTS

Signal substitution is one of the two *dynamic* service methods, the other one being signal tracing. The term "dynamic checking" means to check the receiver under complete operating conditions. This method should not be resorted to in the case of a faulty receiver until the much simpler method of voltage checking has been tried.

The signal-substitution method requires the use of a standard signal generator. At different points throughout the receiver there are several currents and voltages which are called signals. For example, the carrier current induced in the antenna circuit by the passing radio wave is universally identified as the signal. This current may be flowing at any frequency within the broadcast band. After this carrier signal has been mixed with the local oscillator frequency, an IF current at a fixed frequency is brought into existence and amplified through the two IF amplifier stages. This fixed frequency is almost always 455 kc, and it is not at all uncommon for these IF tank voltages and currents to be referred to as the IF signal, or some derivation of that term.

After the IF signal has been detected, or demodulated, by M2, an audio current and voltage are brought into existence. These are subsequently amplified in the two audio amplifiers and the push-pull output circuit. To these several audio amplifier circuits, the audio voltage and current become the audio signal.

A signal generator must be able to develop appropriate signals at each of these frequencies. Further, the signals so developed at the IF and carrier frequencies must be modulated with an audio signal for reasons which will be made clear. Finally, the signal generator must be able to develop a signal at the highest oscillator frequency which may be encountered—455 kc higher than the upper end of the broadcast band, which extends from 550 to about 1,600 kc.

If the standard voltage checking procedure described previously has failed to reveal any faulty components, signal substitution may be used to reveal which of the amplifier stages are functioning properly. The procedure is to start at the output end of the receiver (the speaker) and apply the type of signal which is normally expected to exist at that point to each point. For instance, a strong audio signal is expected to exist at either of the speaker primary windings. Therefore the signal generator should be adjusted to provide a strong audio output signal, and the output probe from the signal generator should be applied to either end of this primary winding. This will cause an audio current to flow up and down in the primary winding. If the speaker is functioning properly, the applied audio signal will be heard through it. If it is not heard, of course, the speaker itself has failed, and repair or replacement is indicated.

If the speaker is functioning, the signal generator probe should be moved to either end of the secondary winding of T1. This will cause audio current to flow up and down through this winding, and the resultant audio voltage will alternately drive the bases of X7 and X8, causing them to conduct. If these stages are both functioning properly, a much-amplified audio signal will be heard from the speaker. (This should remind us to turn down the volume on the signal generator as we move back through the amplifiers.) If no signal is heard, then the trouble is localized to either X7 or X8.

If the previous test was satisfactory, the push-pull amplifiers may be certified as all right, and the probe should be moved to the base of driver transistor X6 (after again turning down the generator output). If the audio signal is heard from the speaker, X6 is functioning properly, and the probe should be moved to the base of X5. The audio signal from the probe will vary the bias voltage at the base of X5 and cause the desired fluctuations of base-emitter current and collector-emitter current which constitute normal operation of the transistor. If this occurs, the audio signal will again be heard from the speaker, and in relatively few minutes we will have completed our check-out of the entire audio section of the receiver.

Next the detector M2 should be checked for normal operation. The selector switch on the signal generator should now be set to deliver an intermediate frequency of 455 kc modulated at an audio frequency which is usually 400 cycles per second. This selector switch position may be labeled MCW, which stands for *modulated continuous wave*.

The generator probe should now be placed at the upper end of the secondary winding of L5. The IF output of the signal generator will drive current up and down through this winding, alternately making the top of the winding more positive and less positive. This winding is connected directly to the power-supply winding line at the bottom of the diagram, which places a permanent positive voltage on the anode of M2 so that the detector current shown in dotted blue flows continuously. When the anode is made more positive by the signal generator voltage, an additional pulsation of detector current will flow. Thus the signal from the generator performs the same function as is performed by an IF signal coupled from L5 when the set is operating normally. If the M2 is operating when this test is made, it will demodulate the 400-cycle audio signal from the artificial IF signal, and a 400-cycle note will be amplified through the four audio amplifiers and will be heard from the speaker.

The generator probe should next be applied to the base of the second IF amplifier X4. The selector switch should remain in the MCW position so that a modulated IF voltage is produced. This voltage will alternately raise and lower the positive voltage at the base of X4, in exactly the same manner as a normal IF signal would. These changes in bias voltage will cause the two currents flowing through X4 to fluctuate at the intermediate frequency. If this stage is operating properly, the oscillating tank current shown in dotted red will be set up and sustained in the tank circuit composed of the primary of L5 and its associated capacitor. The strength of this oscillation will be varied at the 400-cycle rate in accordance with the peaks and troughs of modulation, and since we have already established that all following detector and amplifier stages are functioning properly, the 400-cycle note will be demodulated, and heard from the speaker.

The test for X2 is performed exactly as it was for X4, after first readjusting downward the output level of the signal generator. The IF oscillating current in the collector tank circuit (shown in dotted red) will come into existence if the entire X2 amplifier stage is operating properly, all following amplifier stages will be activated, and the 400-cycle note will be heard from the speaker.

When the converter stage is tested, the possibility that either one of the two tuned circuits may have become inoperative must be recognized. We may make an initial assumption that the oscillator tank is operative, and then attempt to apply a carrier signal to the base of X1. (The frequency setting of the generator should be set as close as possible to the frequency indicated by the tuning dial on the radio.) It may be necessary to tune the signal generator frequency slowly back and forth in this range to find the exact frequency which will mix with the oscillator frequency and produce the 455-kc IF.

If a 400-cycle note comes from the speaker, it indicates that the oscillator tank, transistor X1, and the tank circuit composed of L3 and its associated capacitor are functioning properly. This leaves the antenna tank circuit and the coupling mechanism from this tank, namely, capacitor C3 and the secondary winding of L1 as possible failure items. The generator probe should be moved first to the left hand terminal of C3, and if the signal is still heard, we know that C3 has not failed. Then the probe should be placed at the top of the primary of L1 so that it excites an oscillation of electrons in this tank. This oscillation would correspond to the current shown in dotted blue in Figs. 7-1 and 7-2. If the 400-cycle note is still heard, then this tuned circuit and the transformer coupling across L1 may be considered satisfactory.

If no output comes from the speaker when the artificial signal is applied to the base of X1, it can mean one of two things; either X1 is not conducting electrons, or the oscillator tank is failing to oscillate at its assigned frequency. It is not likely that *both of* these failures will have occurred simultaneously, so let's assume that the oscillator tank has failed. This assumption can quickly be validated by setting the signal generator to a frequency 455 kc higher than the setting on the radio tuning dial, and applying the generator probe to the top of the primary of L2. If still no signal is heard, one of the components in this tank has probably failed. The tank capacitor may be shorted, or the inductor winding may have an open circuit. In making this test, it will probably be necessary to rock the tuning dial of the signal generator slowly back and forth.

## REVIEW QUESTIONS

1. Name and describe the seven principal currents in the transistorized receiver in Fig. 7-1.

2. Which of the two main currents through a transistor controls or regulates the other transistor current and how is the amount of this controlling current regulated?

3. Describe the complete path of the oscillator-emitter current through transistor X1.

4. How is the biasing voltage at the base of transistor X6 obtained?

5. Trace the path of the detector current (shown in dotted blue), citing each component through which it flows. Also state what function the current performs.

6. Explain how an audio voltage is made to appear on the right hand plate of C12 in Fig. 7-1.

7. Trace the paths of collector-emitter currents through X7 and X8. Are they direct or pulsating, and if so, at what frequency?

8. Explain the function of the overload limiter and describe the electron currents that make it possible for this function to be accomplished.

148

Chapter 8

# TUNED RADIO-FREQUENCY RECEIVER

The tuned radio-frequency (TRF) receiver differs from the vast majority of receivers in use today in that it does not utilize the heterodyne principle. As is pointed out in Chapter 1, the heterodyne principle is a frequency-changing process, in which two signals are "beat" against each other to obtain a new third frequency, called the "intermediate frequency." The manifold advantages inherent in this process have led to its adoption in virtually all receiver functions—AM and FM broadcast receivers, TV and radar receivers, and many communications and special purpose receivers.

The principal advantage of generating a fixed value of intermediate frequency in a heterodyne receiver is that all IF amplifier stages can be fixed-tuned, rather than variable-tuned. This enables each such amplifier circuit to be engineered for peak performance at the chosen fixed frequency, with little opportunity for or possibility of maladjustment by an operator.

## TYPICAL TRF RECEIVER

The TRF receiver found its greatest popularity in the early days of radio, before frequency-converting circuits or principles were highly developed. Figs. 8-1 and 8-2 show a typical TRF receiver circuit. There are three tuned circuits in the receiver, one being connected to the control grid of each of the first three amplifier tubes, V1, V2, and V3. The tuning elements, usually one capacitor from each tank, must be mechanically connected together, or ganged, so that when one circuit is tuned to a new frequency, the other two tank circuits will also be tuned to the same frequency.

The third amplifier, V3, utilizes the principle of grid-leak detection to demodulate the audio signal directly from the RF carrier signal. From this point on the audio section of the receiver functions exactly as a comparable audio section in a conventional heterodyne receiver.

Fig. 8-1 differs from 8-2 in that a series diode limiting circuit, constructed around diode V5, has been added to Fig. 8-2 to illustrate a typical application of the noise limiting function.

## Identification of Components

The individual circuit components and their principal functions are as follows:

R1, R4, R9, R12, R14 (Fig. 8-2)—Cathode-biasing resistors.
R2, R5, R13—Screen-grid voltage-dropping resistors.
R3, R6—Power-supply decoupling resistors.
R7—Grid-leak biasing and driving resistor for V3.
R8—AVC resistor.
R10—Plate-load resistor for V3.
R11—Volume control potentiometer.
R15 (Fig. 8-2)—Noise-limiter control potentiometer.
R16 (Fig. 8-2)—Grid-driving resistor for V4.
C1, C2—Tuning capacitors for first RF tank.
C3, C8, C17—Cathode-bypass capacitors.
C4, C9, C16—Screen-grid filter capacitors.
C5, C10—Power-supply decoupling capacitors.
C6, C7—Tuning capacitors for second RF tank.
C11—Tuning capacitor for third RF tank.
C12, C14, C18 (Fig. 8-2), C19 (Fig. 8-2)—Coupling and blocking capacitors.
C13—Plate RF bypass capacitor for V3.
C15—AVC storage capacitor.
L1 (Fig. 8-2)—Radio-frequency choke.
T1, T2, T3—Radio-frequency transformers.
T4—Audio output transformer.
V1, V2—Radio-frequency amplifier tubes.
V3—Grid-leak detector and audio-amplifier tube.
V4—Audio power-amplifier tube.
V5 (Fig. 8-2)—Diode noise-limiter tube.
M1—Power supply.

## Identification of Currents

The several "families" of currents which flow in the TRF receiver all have familiar counterparts in the superhet receiver discussed in Chapter 6. These current families are:

1. Cathode heating current (not shown).
2. Three RF tank currents (solid blue).
3. Five tube plate currents (solid red).
4. Three screen-grid currents (also in solid red).
5. Three cathode filter currents (two in dotted blue; one in dotted green).
6. Three screen-grid filter currents (two in dotted blue; one in dotted green).
7. Two power-supply filter currents (also in dotted blue).
8. One plate-filtering current (also in dotted blue).
9. Three audio-signal currents (solid green).
10. AVC current (dotted green).

## Details of Operation

The cathode heating currents are not shown in Fig. 8-1 and 8-2. It is common practice to omit the filament windings in circuit diagram, because the filament circuit is isolated both electrically and functionally from the remainder of the circuits in a radio. It is universally taken for granted that tube cathodes must be heated before the tubes can perform their normal function of conducting electrons.

Each of the three RF tank currents flows up and down through the secondary winding of its respective RF transformers (T1, T2, or T3); each is sustained in oscillation by the RF current flowing in the associated primary winding. Note that unlike the transformers employed in superheterodyne receivers, the primaries of the coupling transformers are not tuned by a capacitor. In the case of T1, an RF alternating current flows back and forth from the antenna to the primary winding. In the case of T2 and T3, the primary winding currents are pulsating direct currents, since they are the plate currents of V1 and V2, respectively, and these pulsations occur at the radio frequency being received.

All of the amplifier tubes have been biased with grid and cathode voltages so that the tubes will operate under Class-A conditions, which means that each tube conducts electrons continuously throughout an entire cycle of RF or audio voltage. Each plate current (shown in solid red) starts at the ground below the cathode and flows up through the cathode resistor, through the tube from cathode to plate, out the plate and through the

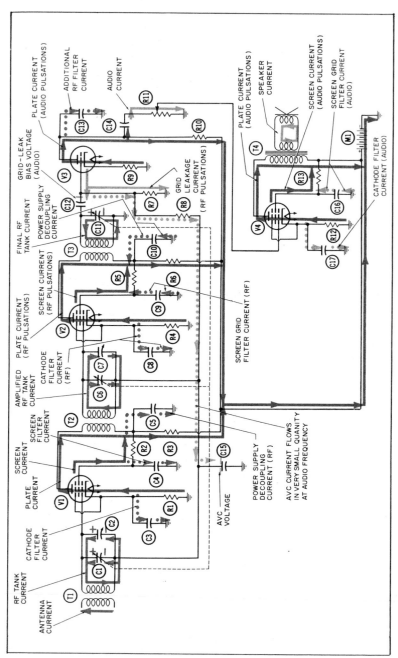

Fig. 8-1. Operation of a typical TRF receiver.

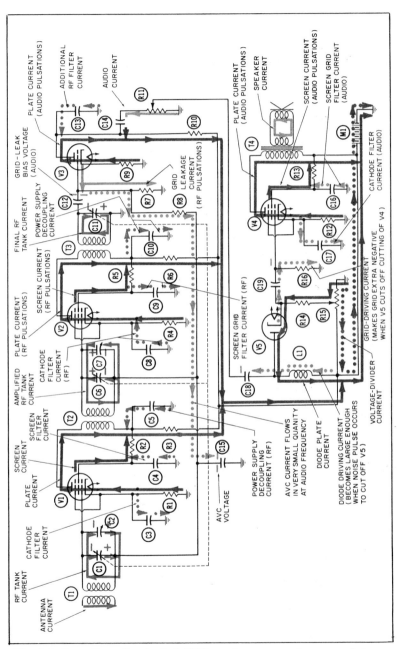

Fig. 8-2. Operation of a typical TRF receiver—currents reversed from those in Fig. 8-1 and a noise limiter added.

153

plate load to the positive terminal of the power supply, then through the power supply to ground.

The three pentode tubes (V1, V2, and V4) also have screen-grid currents. These currents, which have also been shown in solid red, flow out the screen-grid terminal and through the screen-grid resistor where they join the plate currents and flow through the B+ line to the positive terminal of the power supply.

The plate currents through V1 and V2 pulsate at the radio-frequency being received, while the plate currents through V3 and V4 pulsate at the frequency of the audio intelligence which is carried by the carrier signal. The current through V5 flows continuously as long as the incoming signal strength is not made excessive by unwanted noise pulses. When the diode current is flowing, it also pulsates at the audio frequency being demodulated from the carrier.

There are nine separate filter currents in the circuit of Figs. 8-1 and 8-2. Filter currents have been explained many times previously, so they will not be repeated here. Each pulsates back and forth, alternately storing and drawing electrons away from the top plate according to the needs of the circuit to which it is connected. A corresponding electron current flows up from ground to the lower capacitor plate or from the capacitor to ground, in step with the electron flow to or from the upper plate.

The first two cathode filter currents flow at the RF rate in and out of C3 and C8 (shown in dotted blue). The third cathode filter current (shown in dotted green) is at the audio rate, and flows in and out of C17. Likewise, the first two screen grid filter currents (also shown in dotted blue) are RF currents and flow in and out of C4 and C9. The other screen-grid filter current flows at the audio rate in and out of C16 (dotted green).

The two power-supply decoupling currents are shown in dotted blue and flow in and out of C5 and C10 to prevent RF variations from existing on the B+ line. Another filtering current flows in and out of C13 in the plate circuit of V3 to remove the RF pulsations following detection.

The three audio-signal currents (shown in solid green) carry the audio signal from the point of demodulation on C12 to the speaker. These are the grid leakage current from V3 to C12, which pulsates downward through R7, the two-way audio current which flows up and down through R11, and the two-way audio current flowing back and forth through the closed speaker circuit.

The AVC current, shown in dotted green, flows back and forth through R8 at the basic audio frequency being demodulated. The amount of this current which flows during a single half cycle is very slight, because R8 has a very high resistive value. It is this current which delivers electrons to C15, and thereby builds up the negative AVC voltage. The AVC current can be looked upon as an "equalizing" current, since it attempts constantly to equalize the stored voltages at the opposite ends of R8. These voltages are the instantaneous audio voltage on the right hand plate of C12, and the AVC voltage on C15. When the voltage on C12 is more negative than that on C15 (during the modulation peaks), the AVC current flows downward through R8. When the voltage on C12 is less negative than that on C15 (during a modulation trough), the AVC current flows upward through R8.

A little reflection leads to the conclusion that the AVC voltage on C15 will always tend to stabilize at the *average* voltage existing on C12. In other words, this voltage will be midway between the trough and peak values. An example or two may serve to clarify this conclusion. First, imagine an instance where the audio voltage on C12 varies between −2 and −4 volts. (This is identified as the grid leak bias voltage in Fig. 8-1 and 8-2). This voltage will be (−2) volts during a modulation trough, and −4 volts during a modulation peak a half of an audio cycle later. The AVC voltage will tend to assume the average value of these two voltages, or −3 volts. This voltage will be applied directly to the control grids of V1 and V2 as part of their over-all "bias" voltages.

Now imagine that the signal strength increases due to some peculiar atmospheric condition. The three RF tank currents will all be proportionately increased in strength, and the amount of grid-leak detector current flowing out of V3 each cycle will also be increased. As a result, the electron accumulation on the right hand plate of C12 will be proportionately increased, so that the new trough and peak voltages will now be −3 and −6 volts, respectively. The average of these values is −4.5 volts; this is the amount of voltage which will build up on C15 under the new conditions. This increased negative voltage applied to the control grids of V1 and V2 will reduce their over-all gains, and will largely compensate for the unwanted increase in signal strength.

### Noise-Limiting Diode Operation

V5 is connected as a series noise limiter, and functions in substantially the same manner as described in Chapter 3. R15 acts a voltage divider to "bias" the plate of V5 more positively than the cathode. This biasing action is accomplished by the voltage divider current shown in dotted red in Fig. 8-2. Because the point midway along R15 where the cathode voltage is tapped off will always be more negative than the left-hand terminal of R15, the diode plate current shown in solid red will flow continuously along the indicated path unless interrupted by some other action.

During the modulation peaks and troughs which characterize all audio voltages, the amount of diode current through V5 will be increased and decreased. These variations in current flow through R14 will cause the positive voltage at the upper end of the resistor to increase and decrease at the same audio frequency. These audio voltage fluctuations will be coupled across C19 to R16, the grid driving resistor for V4.

When diode current through R14 and V5 increases during modulation peaks, electron current will be drawn upward through R16, making the control grid of V4 positive. When the diode current decreases during modulation troughs, electron current will be driven downward through R16, making the control grid of V4 negative.

Diode V5 can be cut off entirely only by an excessively strong noise pulse having a negative polarity when it reaches the plate of V5. Such a pulse makes the plate of V5 more negative than the cathode, and the upward current flow through R14 is stopped. The positive voltage at the cathode then decreases to the same value existing at the tap on R15. This drop in positive voltage at the upper end of R14 drives a large electron current downward through R16, making the grid of V4 sufficiently negative to cut off this tube entirely and noise limiting has been accomplished.

With the exception of the circuits just discussed—detector, AVC, and noise limiter—the circuits in the TRF receiver are amplifier circuits which are discussed more fully in other chapters of this book or in *Amplifier Circuit Actions*, an earlier volume in this series.

### REVIEW QUESTIONS

1. In the TRF receiver of Figs. 8-1 and 8-2, describe the movements and complete paths of those currents which drive or sustain the electron currents oscillating in the three grid tank circuits.

2. At what point in this receiver does the audio voltage become clearly identifiable as a separate voltage, no longer being "carried" by the carrier frequency?

3. Describe the movements (what makes it flow, and what is its complete path) of that electron current which delivers electron charge to (or withdraws it from) the upper plate of capacitor C15. In which direction does this current flow during a modulation trough? During a modulation peak?

4. Make a comparison between alternate half cycles of this current, during a period of signal fade. How about during a signal build?

5. What is the principal function of the voltage divider current (shown in dotted red) which flows through R15?

6. If the plate of diode V5 becomes more negative than its cathode, explain how a heavy pulsation of plate current through triode V3, which constitutes a negative noise pulse, acts in order to cut off the diode V5.

# INDEX

Shunt-diode noise limiter, 61-65

Signal, normal expected, 118-121

Signal build-up, 45-46

Signal current, 7, 31

Signal fading, 44

Signal generator requirements, 118

Signal substitution, 118-121, 145-148

Second detector, 35

Series-diode noise limiter, 65-72

Speaker action, 111-112

Squelch circuit, 77-81

Sum frequency, 11

Superhet radio, voltage checking of, 112-118

Superregenerative receiver, 97-103

Sustaining oscillations, 26

## T

Tank current, 25-26, 32, 100-101

Tickler-coil oscillator, 16

Time constants, 57-58, 86

Time periods, AVC circuit, 53

Transformer, action, 21-24
output, 110-111

Transistor, biasing, 128-132
broadcast receiver, 122-148
signal substitution checks, 145-148
voltage and resistance checks, 142-145

TRF receiver, 149-156

Triode mixer, 7-12

Tuned radio frequency receiver, 149-156

## V

Voltage, audio, 38-39
AVC, 28, 44-46, 107-108
positive, generation of, 46-60
-divider current, 49, 79-80
grid-leak bias, 24, 94, 96
modulation, 39
oscillating tank, 25
ripple, 87-88

Voltage and resistance checks, transistor receiver, 142-145

Voltage amplifier, 42-43

Voltage checking, superhet radio, 112-118

## Z

Zero beat, 34